HAMPTON-BROWN
HIGH POINT
SUCCESS IN LANGUAGE • LITERATURE • CONTENT

Unit Tests
e-Assessment Edition

LEVEL B

HAMPTON-BROWN

VOCABULARY

DIRECTIONS Read each item carefully. Then choose the best answer. Mark your answer.

1 **Large** is another word for —
- (A) big
- (B) old
- (C) lazy
- (D) happy

2 An **apple** is a kind of —
- (F) rock
- (G) food
- (H) flower
- (J) animal

3 A **bike** is something that you —
- (A) eat
- (B) ride
- (C) sing
- (D) read

4 To **talk** means to —
- (F) take
- (G) look
- (H) hear
- (J) speak

5 When you **buy** something, you —
- (A) build it
- (B) listen to it
- (C) remember it
- (D) pay money for it

6 **Yellow** is a —
- (F) plant
- (G) color
- (H) season
- (J) number

DIRECTIONS Read the sentences in each box. Then read the item carefully. Choose the best answer. Mark your answer.

7
> Rita **adores** that song. She wants to listen to it again and again.

To **adore** something is to —
- (A) like it a lot
- (B) get tired of it
- (C) understand it
- (D) think it is terrible

8
> Raj looks all over the map for Silver Lake. Finally he **locates** it.

When you **locate** something, you —
- (F) eat it
- (G) find it
- (H) cover it
- (J) change it

© Hampton-Brown

2 | Practice Test

GO ON ➤

READING AND LITERARY ANALYSIS

DIRECTIONS Read the passage. Then read each item carefully. Choose the best answer. Mark your answer.

My Dad's Job

My father drives a taxi. He loves his job because it is interesting. Every day he meets different people. He drives them all around the city. Most of the people are tourists, so they ask Dad a lot of questions. They also tell Dad about their lives. He likes that a lot.

Last week, Dad met a very interesting person. One of his passengers was a tall man with dark hair. Dad thought he knew him. The man said that he was a movie actor. Then he and Dad talked about one of their favorite things—the movies!

9 Dad likes his job because —
Ⓐ he can drive fast
Ⓑ the taxi is very big
Ⓒ the work is interesting
Ⓓ he drives to the movies

10 How are Dad and the actor alike?
Ⓕ Both drive a taxi.
Ⓖ Both have dark hair.
Ⓗ Both like the movies.
Ⓙ Both are in the movies.

LANGUAGE SKILLS

DIRECTIONS Read the passage. Then read each item carefully. Choose the best answer. Mark your answer.

Mango and the Blue Jay

My new cat Mango ran into the house. he looked scared. Something had been chasing
_____
1
him. I looked out the door. A big blue jay was sitting on the fence. "Squawk!" the bird cried.

Mango started to go outside again. Suddenly the jay flew toward him and squawked. Poor Mango! He hid in the house.

I watched the bird fly away. It landed on a branch in a pine tree. I noticed a nest. Then I knew why the jay had chased Mango. It <u>were</u>
2
protecting its eggs.

It took a few weeks for the eggs to hatch and for the little birds to grow up. Then Mango was able to go outside in peace again!

11 Number 1 is best written —
Ⓐ he looked scared!
Ⓑ he looked scared?
Ⓒ He looked scared.
Ⓓ as it is written

12 In number 2, <u>were</u> is best written —
Ⓕ be
Ⓖ am
Ⓗ was
Ⓙ as it is written

© Hampton-Brown

GO ON ▶

WRITING

DIRECTIONS Read the draft of the paragraph that Yoko wrote. Then read each item carefully. Choose the best answer. Mark your answer.

My Favorite Sport

(1) Baseball is my favorite sport. (2) During baseball season, I watch all the games on TV. (3) I know all the teems and players. (4) I love to play baseball, too. (5) My friends and I play in the park every Saturday. (6) It is so much fun. (7) I love to hit the ball and go around the bases. (8) I love to swim, too. (9) Maybe I'll be a baseball player when I grow up.

13 What change, if any, should be made in sentence 3?
- Ⓐ Change *know* to **no**
- Ⓑ Change *teems* to **teams**
- Ⓒ Change *players* to **player's**
- Ⓓ Make no change

14 Yoko wants to replace *go* in sentence 7 with a clearer verb. Which one should she choose?
- Ⓕ see
- Ⓖ run
- Ⓗ start
- Ⓙ walk

15 Which sentence does <u>not</u> belong in the paragraph?
- Ⓐ Sentence 1
- Ⓑ Sentence 2
- Ⓒ Sentence 5
- Ⓓ Sentence 8

© Hampton-Brown

STOP

Get the Message!

Section 1: Reading and Language

VOCABULARY

DIRECTIONS Read each item carefully. Then choose the best answer. Mark your answer.

1 When you <u>concentrate</u>, you —
Ⓐ go for a walk
Ⓑ make a decision
Ⓒ think about one thing
Ⓓ meet a group of people

2 <u>Experience</u> is something a person —
Ⓕ looks at
Ⓖ makes up
Ⓗ likes best
Ⓙ lives through

3 Someone who is <u>inspired</u> is —
Ⓐ tired and lazy
Ⓑ filled with ideas
Ⓒ too busy to write
Ⓓ sad about something

4 A <u>legacy</u> is something —
Ⓕ played on a piano
Ⓖ made out of stone
Ⓗ borrowed from someone
Ⓙ handed down from the past

5 A <u>memorial</u> is something that —
Ⓐ moves in a parade
Ⓑ helps soldiers fight a war
Ⓒ helps people remember someone
Ⓓ counts the number of people in a country

6 <u>Memory</u> is the ability to —
Ⓕ make up stories
Ⓖ lift heavy objects
Ⓗ get along with people
Ⓙ think of things from the past

7 The purpose of a <u>monument</u> is to —
Ⓐ explain a belief or an idea
Ⓑ honor a person or an event
Ⓒ provide offices for workers
Ⓓ make someone rich and famous

8 <u>Motive</u> is another word for —
Ⓕ reason
Ⓖ promise
Ⓗ invention
Ⓙ movement

9 When you <u>portray</u> something, you —
Ⓐ give it as a gift
Ⓑ find out about it
Ⓒ make a picture of it
Ⓓ take it to another place

10 <u>Receive</u> means —
Ⓕ get
Ⓖ step
Ⓗ repeat
Ⓙ return

11 If one thing <u>represents</u> another thing, it is —
Ⓐ a letter to it
Ⓑ a report on it
Ⓒ a present for it
Ⓓ an example of it

12 When you <u>launch</u> a rocket, you —
Ⓕ take photos of it
Ⓖ build it as a team
Ⓗ send it into space
Ⓙ draw the plans for it

13 When you have a <u>routine</u>, you —
Ⓐ follow a road map
Ⓑ do something very slowly
Ⓒ share a solution to a problem
Ⓓ always do something the same way

14 A <u>village</u> is —
Ⓕ larger than a city
Ⓖ taller than a house
Ⓗ wider than a valley
Ⓙ smaller than a town

15 When you write a <u>tribute</u>, you —
Ⓐ tell a secret
Ⓑ ask for a favor
Ⓒ express thanks
Ⓓ solve a problem

© Hampton-Brown

GO ON ➡

DIRECTIONS Read the passage. Then read each item carefully. Choose the best answer.
Mark your answer.

The Boy Who Liked to Draw

Far away in the town of Rovia lived two brothers, Carl and Harry. Carl could run and wrestle better than any other person in town. When Carl spoke, people listened to him, but no one looked up to Harry.

Unlike his brave brother, Harry was timid. He was always alone in the woods with his sketchbook. Harry liked to draw pictures from his imagination. In his pictures, he won battles against hairy giants, one-eyed spacemen, and other scary creatures. In his pictures, Harry was always the victor.

One day, Carl and his friends went mountain climbing. Most of the adults were away on their fishing boats. Several adults were left to care for the children. Suddenly, a boat landed on the beach nearby. Six pirates jumped off the boat and headed toward Rovia. Carl spotted them from the mountain and shouted down to the townspeople, but they could not hear his warnings.

Meanwhile, Harry was returning home from the woods. The pirates grabbed Harry's sketchbook. They looked at the pictures. Then they looked at Harry with dread and ran away.

By evening when the townspeople returned, Harry was renowned throughout the town. He was everyone's new hero.

16 Timid means —
- (F) cold and dark
- (G) clever and bold
- (H) shy and frightened
- (J) dangerous and scary

17 Victor means —
- (A) person
- (B) winner
- (C) brother
- (D) creature

18 Dread means —
- (F) fear
- (G) anger
- (H) hunger
- (J) happiness

19 Renowned means —
- (A) lost
- (B) seen
- (C) famous
- (D) disliked

© Hampton-Brown

GO ON ▶

READING AND LITERARY ANALYSIS

DIRECTIONS Read the passage. Then read each item carefully. Choose the best answer.
Mark your answer.

Sisters in a Storm

Lily grabbed the remote control and flopped down on the couch. *Click! Click! Click!* Suddenly the words *Welcome to Star Quest!* blared out from the screen.

"Could you turn it down a little?" Lily's little sister, Kim, asked. She had been reading a book in the den before Lily barged in.

"Shh, be quiet!" Lily hissed.

An icy winter wind howled around the house and rattled the windowpanes. "I think a big storm is coming," Kim said. When Lily didn't answer, she felt sad, as if she and her sister were strangers.

"Will it be smooth-crooning Miguel or rapping Max tonight?" the *Star Quest* host yelled.

The noise blaring from the TV cut into Kim's concentration. She sighed and closed her book. "Which one is which?" she asked, staring at the singers on the screen.

Lily rolled her eyes. "You don't *know*?"

Just then a huge gust of wind shook the house and the electricity snapped off, turning the room into dark silence. Dad rushed in with a flashlight. Then Mom hurried in with candles. Soon fingers of yellow light flickered against the walls.

"What are we going to do now?" Lily groaned.

"I think this a perfect time for you two girls to do something together," Mom said.

"I agree," Dad said, returning with a plate of cookies.

Kim was really happy to have the chance to talk to her sister. "Which singer do you like best, Lily?" she asked. "Miguel or Max?"

She laughed when Lily impersonated both singers and then explained why she was rooting for Max. Then she told Lily about the science book she was reading. It was about some astronauts.

"That sounds interesting," Lily said. "I didn't know you liked space stuff."

About an hour later the lights surged back on and noises screeched from the TV. Lily turned it off. "What were you telling me about your science book, Kim?" she asked.

20 **Where does the story take place?**

(F) at school

(G) in a house

(H) at a TV show

(J) outside in a storm

21 **What is Kim's problem?**

(A) She is afraid of stormy weather.

(B) She does not like the show *Star Quest*.

(C) She is bored by the book she is reading.

(D) She feels as if she and Lily are strangers.

22 **What does Kim really want to do?**

(F) talk to her sister

(G) read more books

(H) watch TV with Lily

(J) go outside and play

23 **What happens after the power comes back on?**

(A) Lily watches TV again.

(B) Lily keeps talking to Kim.

(C) Lily helps Kim do her homework.

(D) Lily reads a book about astronauts.

GO ON ➡

© Hampton-Brown

DIRECTIONS Read the paragraphs and the Venn Diagram. Then read each item carefully. Choose the best answer. Mark your answer.

Koy and Stacy

Koy and Stacy are best friends. They have some special interests in common. Both Koy and Stacy speak Laotian. They both like to write in their diaries.

The two friends like music, too. Koy loves to play the guitar and the piano. She likes to express her feelings through music and poetry. Stacy, however, does not play an instrument. Instead, she loves to dance. She is in the Dance Club and studies ballet. She loves modern dances that tell a story.

Venn Diagram

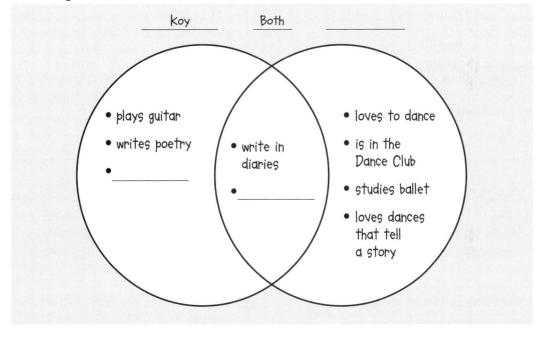

24 Look at the Venn diagram. Which is the best heading for the circle on the right?

   Ⓕ Koy

   Ⓖ Stacy

   Ⓗ Both Stacy and Koy

   Ⓙ Both Koy and Stacy

25 Look at the Venn diagram. How is Koy different from Stacy?

   Ⓐ Koy keeps a diary.

   Ⓑ Koy studies ballet.

   Ⓒ Koy loves to dance.

   Ⓓ Koy plays the guitar.

26 Which of these belongs in the space where the circles overlap?

   Ⓕ like movies

   Ⓖ write poetry

   Ⓗ speak Laotian

   Ⓙ play an instrument

27 Which of these belongs in the space under Koy?

   Ⓐ joins clubs

   Ⓑ tells stories

   Ⓒ plays piano

   Ⓓ studies writing

DIRECTIONS Read the passage. Then read each item carefully. Choose the best answer.
Mark your answer.

Code Talkers

Codes, or secret messages, have been used in battles throughout history. Toward the end of World War I, two Native American soldiers helped create a new kind of code. As they spoke into a field telephone during a battle, their voices sounded all mixed up. To the Germans who were listening, their conversation made no sense at all. What were the men saying? Their voices sounded like a lot of radio static.

The soldiers, Mitchell Bobb and Ben Carterby, were speaking a "code" they knew very well. It was their native language — Choctaw.

The code changed the course of the battle. Unable to crack the code and figure out what the American troops were doing, the Germans soon retreated. Thanks to the Choctaw Code Talkers, the Americans were victorious.

After the war, Mitchell Bobb and Ben Carterby returned home to the United States. Few people knew about the code these men had used and that had helped win a battle.

During World War II, another Native American language—Navajo—was used as a secret code. To indicate the letter *b*, for example, Code Talkers would take an English word that begins with *b*, such as *barrel*, and translate it into its Navajo equivalent, *toish-jeh*. It was the only code used during the war that the enemy could not crack.

28 **What do Code Talkers do?**
- Ⓕ draw maps
- Ⓖ build weapons
- Ⓗ help the enemy
- Ⓙ pass secret messages

29 **Why was the Choctaw "code" so successful?**
- Ⓐ The code was sent over telephone lines.
- Ⓑ The Germans could not understand Choctaw.
- Ⓒ All the American soldiers could understand Choctaw.
- Ⓓ The code used Choctaw words in a different order.

30 **Why were the Code Talkers important?**
- Ⓕ They helped win battles.
- Ⓖ They were Native Americans.
- Ⓗ They used their native languages.
- Ⓙ They returned home after the war.

31 **Which of these sentences tells the main idea of the passage?**
- Ⓐ American troops learned Choctaw during World War I.
- Ⓑ Native American soldiers spoke Navajo during wartime.
- Ⓒ German soldiers spoke foreign languages during World War II.
- Ⓓ Native American languages were used as secret codes during wartime.

© Hampton-Brown

GO ON ➡

DIRECTIONS Read each poem. Then read each item carefully. Choose the best answer. Mark your answer.

Summer Evening

1 I sit outside next to Dad.
He snores softly in his favorite chair.
The warm air and sound of the sprinkler
    put him to sleep.
As crickets sing and shadows dance
    around us,
I think: I will stay on this porch forever.

2 My friend Sofia arrives with other plans.
"Let's lie on the grass, count stars,
    and tell stories," she says.
Her excitement convinces me.
We sing, giggle, and imagine many things.
But before long, it's my turn to sleep.

Laundry Day

1 The sock jingles, filled with quarters.
Dad tells me, "No soda, Tom!"
and "Bring back the change!"
The sun is out,
and I head down to the Wash 'n' Dry.

2 I sit and I wait. I wait and I sit.
Then in comes the lady from
    the drugstore,
who brings me stories, just a little
    candy,
and always makes me smile.

3 We chat and laugh as the clothes turn
in washers, then dryers.
How easy it is to do laundry
with the help of friends.

32 Which of these gives the best summary of stanza 1 of "Summer Evening"?

Ⓕ A girl feels the warm air on a summer evening.

Ⓖ A girl sits outside and waits for her father to wake up.

Ⓗ A girl enjoys a warm summer evening next to her father.

Ⓙ A girl listens to her father's snoring, a sprinkler, and crickets.

33 Which of these gives the best summary of stanza 2 of "Summer Evening"?

Ⓐ A girl lies on the grass on a summer evening.

Ⓑ A girl and her friend giggle because it is a warm evening.

Ⓒ A girl imagines things while she sleeps on a warm summer evening.

Ⓓ A girl falls asleep after playing with her friend on a warm summer evening.

34 Which of these gives the best summary of stanza 1 of "Laundry Day"?

Ⓕ A father sends his son out to do the laundry.

Ⓖ A father teaches his son how to do the laundry.

Ⓗ A boy carries a sock filled with jingling quarters.

Ⓙ A boy is sad because he has to work on a sunny day.

35 Which of these gives the best summary of "Laundry Day"?

Ⓐ A boy has fun doing laundry with a friend.

Ⓑ A boy finds out that it is hard to do laundry.

Ⓒ A boy decides to do laundry on a sunny day.

Ⓓ A boy eats candy, but does not drink soda while doing laundry.

© Hampton-Brown

GO ON

DIRECTIONS Read the passage. Then read each item carefully. Choose the best answer.
Mark your answer.

Norma is at the park. She want to record the sounds of birds for her science project. Suddenly she sees a tiny metal box with two shiny buttons. A red button and a green button.
    Norma looks down at the big green button. She pushes the red button instead. In a flash, she travels back through time. She go to the ancient city of Rome. The people are wearing beautiful long robes. They speak a different language. Norma recognizes some words from her Latin class. Quickly, she tapes the people's voices with her tape recorder.
    Then she sees the metal box again. The buttons is close to her hand. This time she pushes the green button. Then she is back in the park on Oak Street where she began.
    "Tomorrow, I'll play the tape back for my teacher," she decides.

---

36 In number 1, She want is best written —
   F She wants
   G She wanting
   H She will wants
   J as it is written

37 In number 2, she sees is best written —
   A she see
   B she seed
   C she will see
   D as it is written

38 Number 3 is best written —
   F It has a red button and a green button.
   G A red button and a green button on the top.
   H A big, bright red button and a green button.
   J as it is written

39 The best way to combine the sentences in number 4 is —
   A button or she pushes
   B button, or she pushes
   C button but she pushes
   D button, but she pushes

40 In number 5, She go is best written —
   F She goes
   G She goed
   H She gone
   J as it is written

41 The best way to combine the sentences in number 6 is —
   A long robes, so they speak
   B long robes, for they speak
   C long robes, but they speak
   D long robes, and they speak

42 In number 7, The buttons is is best written —
   F The buttons be
   G The buttons are
   H The buttons was
   J as it is written

43 Which of the following is a complete sentence?
   A Sees the metal box.
   B She travels to Rome.
   C To record the sounds.
   D For her science project.

© Hampton-Brown

STOP

Section 2: Writing

PROCESS AND STRATEGIES

DIRECTIONS Read about the science fiction story Peren plans to write. Then read each item carefully. Choose the best answer. Mark your answer.

> Peren wants to write a science fiction story about a spacewoman. The spacewoman thinks she is phoning her friend in her hometown on planet Xarky. Somehow she dials the number of a police station on planet Earth.

1 The purpose of Peren's story is to —
- Ⓐ inform people about police work
- Ⓑ describe how to reach distant planets
- Ⓒ explain how telephones work in outer space
- Ⓓ tell a fantasy story about a woman from space

2 Now that Peren has her story idea, what should she do first?
- Ⓕ Read more fantasies.
- Ⓖ Plan the events in the plot.
- Ⓗ Write dialogue for the story.
- Ⓙ Write an introduction to the story.

3 Which of these is the best way for Peren to make her characters come alive?
- Ⓐ Use their names.
- Ⓑ Tell how old they are.
- Ⓒ Tell what they are like.
- Ⓓ Use dialogue to show what they are like.

4 What should Peren tell in the ending to the story?
- Ⓕ how the problem started
- Ⓖ where the story takes place
- Ⓗ who the main characters are
- Ⓙ how the problem was resolved

GO ON

DIRECTIONS Read the draft of the story that Peren wrote. Then read each item carefully. Choose the best answer. Mark your answer.

A Friendly Call

(1) Robotica stared up at Xarky in the night sky. (2) Xarky was her home planet. (3) It was a bilion miles from the Galaxy Hotel Station, where she was attending an all-planet business conference.

(4) "I wonder what Cyber is doing?" Robotica said, thinking of her best friend on Xarky. (5) She flipped open her intergalactic communicator and jabbed some buttons. (6) She expected to hear Cyber's voice. (7) Strange sounds filled her ear.

(8) Robotica inserted her universal language disc and the garbled words instantly became clear. (9) "This is officer ling," a voice said in Xarkish, "Parker Police Station, planet Earth."

(10) Robotica explained that she had entered the wrong number. (11) "I was trying to reach my friend Cyber," she said. (12) "He live on Xarky."

(13) "Do you mean Cyber Jupiteria?" the police officer asked.

(14) "Yes," Robotica replied. (15) "Do you know him?"

(16) "I met him on a galaxy tour," the officer said. (17) "Cyber saved me last month from a flying moon rock! (18) I can transfer you," he offered.

(19) Robotica was surprised. (20) Pressed her communicator to her ear and waited. (21) Suddenly, the universe didn't seem so big.

PROCESS AND STRATEGIES, *continued*

5 Peren wants to rewrite sentence 1 to grab her reader's interest. How should she rewrite it?

Ⓐ Robotica, a spacewoman, missed the planet Xarky.

Ⓑ Robotica decided to see if she could see Xarky in the sky.

Ⓒ "There's Xarky," Robotica said one night, as she looked up at a planet in the sky.

Ⓓ "There's no place like Xarky," Robotica sighed, staring up at a twinkle in the night sky.

6 What change, if any, should be made in sentence 3?

Ⓕ Change *miles* to **mile**

Ⓖ Change *bilion* to **billion**

Ⓗ Change *Galaxy Hotel Station* to **galaxy hotel station**

Ⓙ Make no change

7 What is the best way to combine sentences 6 and 7?

Ⓐ She expected to hear Cyber's voice, **or** strange sounds filled her ear.

Ⓑ She expected to hear Cyber's voice, **so** strange sounds filled her ear.

Ⓒ She expected to hear Cyber's voice, **and** strange sounds filled her ear.

Ⓓ She expected to hear Cyber's voice, **but** strange sounds filled her ear.

8 What change, if any, should be made in sentence 9?

Ⓕ Change *a* to **an**

Ⓖ Change *This is* to **This**

Ⓗ Change *officer ling* to **Officer Ling**

Ⓙ Make no change

9 What is the best way to rewrite sentence 10 to add dialogue?

Ⓐ "Listen to me!" Robotica cried in a loud voice.

Ⓑ "What is going on here?" Robotica wondered.

Ⓒ "Sorry! I pushed the wrong buttons!" Robotica replied.

Ⓓ "I need a new intergalactic communicator," Robotica muttered.

10 What change, if any, should be made in sentence 12?

Ⓕ Delete *He*

Ⓖ Change *live* to **lives**

Ⓗ Change *Xarky* to **xarky**

Ⓙ Make no change

11 What is the best way to revise sentence 19 to show how the character feels?

Ⓐ Robotica was really, truly surprised.

Ⓑ Imagine how surprised Robotica was when she heard!

Ⓒ "Do you really know Cyber? Wow! That's amazing!" Robotica said.

Ⓓ No revision is needed.

12 What change, if any, should be made in sentence 20?

Ⓕ Delete *and*

Ⓖ Change *ear* to **eares**

Ⓗ Change *Pressed* to **She pressed**

Ⓙ Make no change

STOP

WRITTEN COMPOSITION: FANTASY STORY

DIRECTIONS Read the writing prompt. Then write your fantasy story on a separate sheet of paper.

WRITING PROMPT

Write a fantasy story for your class to read. Write about a normal, daily event that turns into something that could not really happen.

A Sense of Place

Section 1: Reading and Language

VOCABULARY

DIRECTIONS Read each item carefully. Then choose the best answer. Mark your answer.

1 When you **adjust**, you —
- (A) admit something
- (B) get used to something
- (C) understand something
- (D) refuse to do something

2 A **benefit** is a —
- (F) new friend
- (G) good result
- (H) favorite song
- (J) large bandage

3 When you **celebrate**, you —
- (A) dance and sing
- (B) think and write
- (C) sleep and dream
- (D) argue and discuss

4 To **challenge** something is to —
- (F) sell it to someone
- (G) take a stand against it
- (H) change its appearance
- (J) move it to another place

5 To **compete** is to —
- (A) finish a meal
- (B) take a long trip
- (C) try to win a game
- (D) ask a difficult question

6 A **conversation** is —
- (F) a clever trick
- (G) a friendly talk
- (H) a deep canyon
- (J) an ancient story

7 **Culture** is —
- (A) flowers, plants, and trees
- (B) cities, towns, and countries
- (C) brothers, sisters, and other relatives
- (D) arts, beliefs, and ways of doing things

8 A **custom** is a —
- (F) character in a play
- (G) place where people live
- (H) person who lived long ago
- (J) way of acting that is special to a country

9 When you are **engaged**, you are —
- (A) invited to a party
- (B) promised in marriage
- (C) chosen for an important job
- (D) respected among your friends

10 A **privilege** is a —
- (F) book with family photos
- (G) painting of someone's home
- (H) special thing you are allowed to do
- (J) punishment for doing something wrong

11 Another word for **provide** is —
- (A) supply
- (B) permit
- (C) belong
- (D) portray

12 To **recognize** someone is to —
- (F) give the person a gift
- (G) invite the person to a party
- (H) know the person when you see him or her
- (J) tell when that person does something wrong

13 When you **respect** someone, you —
- (A) ignore that person
- (B) rescue that person
- (C) honor that person highly
- (D) tell stories to that person

14 When you **trade** something, you —
- (F) buy it and fix it
- (G) change it and keep it
- (H) lose it and then find it again
- (J) give it and take something else

15 A **tradition** is —
- (A) planted in a park
- (B) made in a factory
- (C) learned on the Internet
- (D) passed down from ancestors

© Hampton-Brown

GO ON ➤

DIRECTIONS Read the passage. Then read each item carefully. Choose the best answer. Mark your answer.

The Bicycle Bash

I grew up in India, in a place called Old Goa, but my family has been in the United States for a while. On Monday, June 20, we moved into a new house on Grant Street. That afternoon I saw the girl next door. I waved and said "Hi," but she ignored me. I felt terrible. My mom thought she was shy, but I believed she was unfriendly.

On Saturday I saw a sign at the library. It said, "Summer Projects Wanted." I remembered my summers in Old Goa, when I used to ride bikes with all my friends. The sign also said, "See Ms. Johnson." I found Ms. Johnson.

"Hi," I said. "My name is Jasbir, and I'd like to organize a bicycle **bash**." Then I told her my plan. Ms. Johnson thought it was a great idea. She said we could plan it for August 1.

"Now, here is one of our teen workers," she said. "Mariah can help you."

I turned around—and there was my neighbor! She frowned at me.

"I think a bicycle bash is a silly idea," Mariah said. "No one will want to do it!"

"I think it's a good idea. Give Jasbir a chance," said Ms. Johnson.

We were busy in July. Mariah helped, but she talked to me only when she had to. By July 28, everything was ready.

On August 1, kids on bikes came to the library. First we made sure each rider was wearing a helmet. Then we checked the tires and brakes on the bikes. After that we had games and a parade. At the end of the day Ms. Johnson said it was the best project ever. More kids came than for any other summer project.

Then Mariah said, "I guess I've been pretty mean to you. I'm sorry. I just never met anyone before who sounds or looks like you. Will you forgive me?"

"Yes," I said. "Let's ride over to my house for some ice cream."

"Great idea, Jasbir," Mariah smiled. "I love to ride bikes!"

Jasbir and I went riding every day after that. We were both glad to have a new friend.

....

bash a festive event; party

GO ON ➡

READING AND LITERARY ANALYSIS, continued

16 **Which of these phrases lets you know when Jasbir saw Mariah?**

- Ⓕ *I saw*
- Ⓖ *that afternoon*
- Ⓗ *the girl next door*
- Ⓙ *waved and said "Hi"*

17 **Study the time line.**

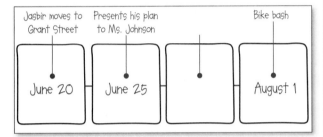

Which of these completes the time line?

- Ⓐ August 2, Clean up
- Ⓑ June 18, Pack boxes
- Ⓒ July 28, Everything ready
- Ⓓ September 6, Start school

18 **If Mariah had told the story, you might —**

- Ⓕ know where Jasbir lives
- Ⓖ know more about her feelings
- Ⓗ understand how to organize a summer project
- Ⓙ understand why the bicycle bash was a success

19 **Suppose that someone who is not in the story is telling it. Which of these sentences should be in the story?**

- Ⓐ Our hometown was in a place called Old Goa.
- Ⓑ My family is from a place in India called Old Goa.
- Ⓒ Jasbir grew up in India, in a place called Old Goa.
- Ⓓ My neighbor asked me if I was from a town called Old Goa.

20 **Which of these sentences from the story is a fact?**

- Ⓕ I felt terrible.
- Ⓖ Kids on bikes came to the library.
- Ⓗ I think a bicycle bash is a silly idea.
- Ⓙ Ms. Johnson thought it was a great idea.

Read the chart. Use it to help you answer items 21 and 22.

Character	Opinion	Signal Words
Jasbir	Mariah was unfriendly.	**21** ____
Mariah	**22** ____	I think

21 **Which of these goes on the blank line in column 3?**

- Ⓐ I believed
- Ⓑ on Grant Street
- Ⓒ Monday, June 20
- Ⓓ the girl next door

22 **Which of these goes on the blank line in column 2?**

- Ⓕ Will you forgive me?
- Ⓖ We were busy in July.
- Ⓗ A bicycle bash is a silly idea.
- Ⓙ She talked to me only when she had to.

GO ON ➡

READING AND LITERARY ANALYSIS, *continued*

DIRECTIONS Read the passage. Then read each item carefully. Choose the best answer. Mark your answer.

Duc: "My Interesting Life"

My family came to the United States from Vietnam when I was eight years old. One of the few things I brought with me was a special rock. It was a small, flat rock, and I used it to play games. Before I left Vietnam, I wrote the date and name of our village on it.

When we first arrived, we lived in Los Angeles. My parents put me in school right away. The special English classes were fun, and it was easy for me to learn English. I even learned some Spanish from playing with the other kids.

That summer, my rock collection got bigger. Whenever we went somewhere, I brought home a new rock. I thought I had the most beautiful rock collection in the world. Looking at my collection helped me remember special places.

After a year, we moved to Chicago. Before we left Los Angeles, my friends gave me a rock with all of their names on it. That was the best present I ever got!

We stayed in Chicago for three years. During that time, I told stories at the school and public libraries. Some of the stories were folk tales from Vietnam. Sometimes I would show my rock collection and tell stories about the places I had visited. My listeners liked hearing about other places, and they said my collection was interesting.

About two years ago, we moved here, to Virginia. On weekends I tell stories at the public library. Next week, the library is going to put my rock collection on display. I'm glad I can share my life with so many people and tell them about my collection.

23 **How old is Duc at the end of the passage?**
- Ⓐ 8 years old
- Ⓑ 9 years old
- Ⓒ 12 years old
- Ⓓ 14 years old

24 **Each sentence below is from the story. Which is an opinion?**
- Ⓕ I would show my rock collection and tell stories.
- Ⓖ I had the most beautiful rock collection in the world.
- Ⓗ My friends gave me a rock with all of their names on it.
- Ⓙ One of the few things I brought with me was a special rock.

25 **What happens last in the story?**
- Ⓐ Duc returns to Vietnam.
- Ⓑ Duc moves to Los Angeles.
- Ⓒ Duc tells his stories at the public library.
- Ⓓ Duc thanks his friends for the special rock.

26 **If Duc's parents had told the story, you might find out why —**
- Ⓕ the listeners like rock stories
- Ⓖ Duc's friends are so thoughtful
- Ⓗ the library displays Duc's rocks
- Ⓙ their family moves so many times

27 **Suppose that someone who is not in the story is telling it. Which of these sentences would be in the story?**
- Ⓐ Duc moved to the United States.
- Ⓑ Our family moved from Los Angeles.
- Ⓒ We stayed in Chicago for three years.
- Ⓓ I moved to Virginia about two years ago.

GO ON ➡

DIRECTIONS Read each item carefully. Then choose the best answer. Mark your answer.

28 Luisa is reading a magazine article. Before she reads, she wants to make a prediction. What should she do first?

(F) Read the article.

(G) Do some research.

(H) Take notes about the article.

(J) Read the title and the introduction.

29 Luisa predicts that she will learn how clubs help teens find friends. Preview the magazine article to see if Luisa's prediction is correct.

Make Friends — Join a Club!

Teens from many countries find a way to make friends soon after they arrive in the United States. They join clubs.

Is Luisa's prediction correct?

(A) No, because the teens in the photograph are not friends.

(B) Yes, because teens make friends when they read magazines.

(C) No, because the introduction talks about teens from other countries.

(D) Yes, because the title and the photograph are about making friends in clubs.

30 Luisa reads the next part of the article.

Meet Nilda Ramos. She arrived in Chicago last year. Read what she says about how teen clubs helped her.

"I did not know anyone except my family when I came to this country," said Nilda. "I was very scared. Then one day my teacher invited me to a meeting of the Computer Club. Every week the club members meet and chat on-line with other clubs. The kids were friendly. Since I already knew how to use the computer, I did not need a lot of English to get started. Then I met two kids who wanted to learn to speak Spanish. I taught them Spanish. They helped me with my English, and we all improved our computer skills! Soon we were looking into other clubs that we could join."

Which of these is the best prediction for Luisa to make next?

(F) Now the article will tell about other clubs.

(G) Now the article will describe the students' families.

(H) Now the article will explain the rules of some games.

(J) Now the article will convince readers to learn English.

31 Which of these lists might Luisa expect to find at the end of the article?

(A) e-mail addresses for online kids' clubs

(B) home addresses of all teens in Chicago

(C) words that look alike in Spanish and English

(D) phone numbers of kids from other countries

© Hampton-Brown

GO ON

DIRECTIONS Read the passage. Then read each item carefully. Choose the best answer. Mark your answer.

The day my grandfather left Sweden was the scariest day of his life. He said goodbye to his family and friends—forever. When his ship <u>sailed</u> into the harbor of New York City,
<u>1</u>
he felt alone.

First my grandfather went to Boston, where <u>her</u> cousin lived. He worked hard as a
<u>2</u>
house painter. He struggled to learn English. Finally he got a job working on railroads.

Then something wonderful happened. My grandfather, Anders Hanson, met my grandmother. <u>She were</u> a waitress in a
<u>3</u>
restaurant in Detroit. He <u>thinked</u> she was the
<u>4</u>
most beautiful woman in the world.

"My name is Anders," he said, politely.

My grandmother said that <u>their</u> name
<u>5</u>
was Louise. She spoke in broken English, like my grandfather, and she had a French accent. She said she was from Canada.

Grandfather smiled. "Someday soon I <u>marry</u> you," he said.
<u>6</u>
A few years later, my grandparents were married. Grandfather made a beautiful wooden chest for my grandmother. <u>Embroidered</u> pillowcases with wildflowers
<u>7</u>
of the Canadian mountains.

Now I have <u>them</u> special chest.
<u>8</u>
Grandmother's pillowcases are folded neatly inside the chest. And inside my heart I have warm memories of my grandparents.

32 In number 1, <u>sailed</u> is best written —
- (F) sails
- (G) will sail
- (H) is sailing
- (J) as it is written

33 In number 2, <u>her</u> is best written —
- (A) its
- (B) his
- (C) him
- (D) as it is written

34 In number 3, <u>She were</u> is best written —
- (F) She was
- (G) Her was
- (H) His was
- (J) as it is written

35 In number 4, <u>thinked</u> is best written —
- (A) thought
- (B) will think
- (C) is thinking
- (D) as it is written

36 In number 5, <u>their</u> is best written —
- (F) her
- (G) she
- (H) its
- (J) as it is written

37 In number 6, <u>marry</u> is best written —
- (A) marries
- (B) to marry
- (C) will marry
- (D) as it is written

38 In number 7, <u>Embroidered</u> is best written —
- (F) She embroidered
- (G) Her embroidered
- (H) Them embroidered
- (J) as it is written

39 In number 8, <u>them</u> is best written —
- (A) they
- (B) their
- (C) theirs
- (D) as it is written

© Hampton-Brown

STOP

Section 2: Writing

PROCESS AND STRATEGIES

DIRECTIONS Read about Antonio's personal history. Then read each item carefully. Choose the best answer. Mark your answer.

> Antonio plans to write a personal history for his classmates to read. He wants to tell about special memories and events in his life.

1 Antonio writes his personal history to —

Ⓐ review facts for a test
Ⓑ practice his handwriting
Ⓒ express his personal feelings
Ⓓ persuade people to take action

2 Each paragraph he writes should —

Ⓕ include a time line
Ⓖ have five sentences
Ⓗ begin with a question
Ⓙ tell about only one topic

3 Antonio begins a paragraph with this topic sentence: "I tried pizza for the first time at my friend's house." Which of these details should he include in his paragraph?

Ⓐ My friend's house has a large kitchen.
Ⓑ Everyone in the family knows how to cook.
Ⓒ Pizza is often served in the lunchroom at school.
Ⓓ I discovered that I love spicy pepperoni and melted cheese.

4 Which of these should Antonio <u>not</u> do when he writes a draft for his personal history?

Ⓕ Tell about his life.
Ⓖ End with some final thoughts.
Ⓗ Worry about making mistakes.
Ⓙ Use pronouns like *I*, *my*, and *us*.

GO ON

PROCESS AND STRATEGIES, *continued*

DIRECTIONS Read the draft of the personal history that Antonio wrote. Then read each item carefully. Choose the best answer. Mark your answer.

No More Shy Guy

(1) When I was a little kid, I was really shy. (2) I had a few friends at school, but I didnt eat lunch with them or anything. (3) I just mumbled "hi" whenever I saw them. (4) "Hi," they mumbled back. (5) They were shy guy's, too!

(6) I was even quiet at home. (7) I never turned on the TV. (8) At dinner I ate quietly. (9) I mostly just listen to my brothers and sisters chatter about their day. (10) I always seemed to be in my room reading. (11) I liked to play the drums in my room, too.

(12) I was walking home from school, past the Mexican restaurant I went by every day. (13) In the vacant lot next to the restaurant, some kids from my block were playing soccer. (14) One guy yelled, "Hey, Antonio, do you want to play?" (15) I wanted to not be shy anymore, so I decided to join the game.

(16) After that, I was a lot friendlier. (17) My cousin Alfredo is the friendly type. (18) I realized that I just couldn't wait for peeple to reach out to me. (19) I had to talk to them. (20) After all, maybe they were shy, too.

© Hampton-Brown

GO ON

PROCESS AND STRATEGIES, *continued*

5 Which of these details fits into the first paragraph after sentence 1?

Ⓐ There are eight people in my family.

Ⓑ I walked to and from school by myself.

Ⓒ I liked to visit my grandparents in the summer.

Ⓓ My friend Ron and I always went to the movies together.

6 What change, if any, should be made in sentence 2?

Ⓕ Change *them* to **they**

Ⓖ Change *didnt* to **didn't**

Ⓗ Delete the comma before *but*

Ⓙ Make no change

7 What change, if any, should be made in sentence 5?

Ⓐ Delete *They*

Ⓑ Change *guy's* to **guys**

Ⓒ Change *They* to **Them**

Ⓓ Make no change

8 Which sentence does <u>not</u> belong in the paragraph that begins with sentence 6?

Ⓕ Sentence 7

Ⓖ Sentence 9

Ⓗ Sentence 10

Ⓙ Sentence 11

9 Which of these is the <u>best</u> topic sentence to add before sentence 12?

Ⓐ Then suddenly my friends changed.

Ⓑ Then one day I was doing what I usually do.

Ⓒ So I decided to talk to my brothers and sisters.

Ⓓ Then one day something happened that made me change.

10 What change, if any, should be made in sentence 9?

Ⓕ Change *my* to **our**

Ⓖ Change *their* to **they're**

Ⓗ Change *listen* to **listened**

Ⓙ Make no change

11 Which sentence does <u>not</u> belong in the last paragraph?

Ⓐ Sentence 16

Ⓑ Sentence 17

Ⓒ Sentence 19

Ⓓ Sentence 20

12 What change, if any, should be made in sentence 18?

Ⓕ Change *peeple* to **people**

Ⓖ Add a comma after *realized*

Ⓗ Change the period to a question mark

Ⓙ Make no change

© Hampton-Brown

STOP

WRITTEN COMPOSITION: PERSONAL NARRATIVE

DIRECTIONS Read the writing prompt, then write your personal narrative on a separate sheet of paper.

WRITING PROMPT

Think about a group to which you belong—your family, your friends, or a club, for example. Write a personal narrative about something important you did together.

Follow Your Dreams

Section 1: Reading and Language

VOCABULARY

DIRECTIONS Read each item carefully. Then choose the best answer. Mark your answer.

1 **Adversity** means —
- Ⓐ past history
- Ⓑ new experience
- Ⓒ difficult situation
- Ⓓ friendly character

2 To be **confident** is to be —
- Ⓕ sure of yourself
- Ⓖ sorry for yourself
- Ⓗ angry with yourself
- Ⓙ surprised at yourself

3 **Craftsmanship** is another word for —
- Ⓐ cost
- Ⓑ goal
- Ⓒ skill
- Ⓓ belief

4 A **debt** is —
- Ⓕ food that is shared
- Ⓖ clothing that is torn
- Ⓗ water that is stored
- Ⓙ money that is owed

5 To be **determined** is to —
- Ⓐ write something in a book
- Ⓑ remember something clearly
- Ⓒ wonder about doing something
- Ⓓ have your mind set on doing something

6 When you **excel** at something, you —
- Ⓕ do it very well
- Ⓖ do it once a year
- Ⓗ need help doing it
- Ⓙ ask others to do it

7 A **merchant** is someone who —
- Ⓐ sails large ships
- Ⓑ raises farm animals
- Ⓒ sells things in a store
- Ⓓ manages workers in a factory

8 A **migration** is a —
- Ⓕ group of workers
- Ⓖ change in the climate
- Ⓗ move from one place to another
- Ⓙ decision made by a government

9 An **opportunity** is a —
- Ⓐ difficult choice
- Ⓑ completed assignment
- Ⓒ description of a person
- Ⓓ chance to do something

10 Something **ordinary** is —
- Ⓕ large
- Ⓖ regular
- Ⓗ perfect
- Ⓙ unusual

11 **Real** means —
- Ⓐ not common
- Ⓑ not imagined
- Ⓒ not completed
- Ⓓ not appropriate

12 When you **replace** something, you —
- Ⓕ give it away
- Ⓖ do it a second time
- Ⓗ save it for later use
- Ⓙ put another thing in its place

13 When there is a **shortage**, there is —
- Ⓐ nothing at all
- Ⓑ too much of something
- Ⓒ not enough of something
- Ⓓ more of something than before

14 **Temporary** means —
- Ⓕ for enough time
- Ⓖ for a limited time
- Ⓗ for a very long time
- Ⓙ for as long as you wish

15 Another word for **triumph** is —
- Ⓐ terror
- Ⓑ victory
- Ⓒ dignity
- Ⓓ contract

© Hampton-Brown

GO ON ➡

DIRECTIONS Read the passage. Then read each item carefully. Choose the best answer. Mark your answer.

The Debate

Soraya Wells stood at the podium and looked out over the sea of faces. It seemed as if the whole school had come to listen to the first round of the Debate Club's spring tournament. Soraya wanted to do well in front of everyone.

As Mr. Jackson, her debate coach, introduced her, Soraya tried to remember the rules for being a good debater. *"Rule One: smile when you are introduced,"* she told herself as she smiled nervously at the audience.

When Mr. Jackson introduced her opponent, Olga Martínez, Soraya suddenly wished she weren't on stage. Olga looked as confident as a flag. "I can't do this," Soraya thought miserably. "I'm too shy to be a debater. After this round, I'm going to quit the Debate Club!"

Mr. Jackson stepped forward to announce the subject of the debate: "All students at Stone Creek Middle School should be required to wear uniforms." The students quieted down, and the auditorium grew as silent as a cave.

Mr. Jackson turned to Soraya to present her first argument. She opened her mouth, hoping her voice would come out. *"Rule Two:"* she thought anxiously, *"speak in a loud, clear voice."*

Soraya could hear her soft words as she spoke. She took a deep, shaky breath when she finished speaking. Then Olga presented her argument. Her voice soared over the audience like a strong, beautiful bird.

Soraya wanted to crawl off the stage. Then she thought, "Wait a minute. I *AM* a good debater, or else I wouldn't be in this tournament. Besides, I love to debate. I want to get better! I'm not going to give up."

"Miss Wells?" Mr. Jackson said, indicating that it was time for her second argument. *"Rule Three:"* Soraya told herself, *"relax and enjoy the debate!"*

---

16 Read the sentence in the box.

> The students quieted down, and the auditorium grew as silent as a cave.

Which of these is the best paraphrase of that sentence?

(F) The students talked quietly in the auditorium.

(G) The auditorium was quiet until all the students started to talk.

(H) The students stopped talking, and the auditorium became quiet.

(J) Some students in the auditorium talked, but others were quiet.

17 Read the sentence in the box.

> Soraya wanted to crawl off the stage.

Which of these is the best paraphrase of that sentence?

(A) Soraya fell on the stage.

(B) Soraya wanted to walk up on the stage.

(C) Soraya felt terrible and wanted to leave.

(D) Soraya wished that the audience would leave.

18 What was Soraya's goal?

(F) to join a club

(G) to be a good debater

(H) to recite the debate rules

(J) to make students wear uniforms

GO ON

DIRECTIONS Read the passage. Then read each item carefully. Choose the best answer. Mark your answer.

A Different Assignment

Mr. Yamaguchi was smiling when class began. "You are going to like this weekend's assignment. Next week we'll be working outside of school on a community project, and you're going to pick it." He told the class to read the weekend newspaper for ideas.

On Monday, groups met and shared their ideas. Then they presented their best ideas to the class. Luis shared an article about an animal shelter that needed help feeding and taking care of stray dogs and cats. He suggested that the class help the shelter. Everyone endorsed the idea, except Lena, who complained, "I'm allergic to cats!"

The other students were excited. Marta said, "We can have a family fun night and charge each person two cans of dog or cat food." Other students suggested having pizza, games, and prizes, and even a storytelling center for folk tales about animals. They also talked about organizing volunteers who would walk and feed the cats and dogs at the shelter.

Mr. Yamaguchi beamed. He was proud and told the class, "Congratulations. You all have excellent ideas. Now the hard work begins." He explained that they would need to share the work. Luis's group would write the advertisements for the newspaper. Lena decided to lead the group that would write the invitations. Kate's group would write folk tales to share.

The class worked hard every day planning, writing, and reporting their progress. At last the big evening came. People poured into the classroom like a great flood. Each one carried cans of dog or cat food. It was a great success!

The best part came at the end when Luis gave a speech and presented all the food to the shelter's director, Ms. Taylor. When Luis finished the speech, his classmates knew that they had made a difference. Angie had tears in her eyes, and Mr. Yamaguchi smiled. His students had learned the power of community involvement.

---

19 Read the sentence in the box.

> Luis shared an article about an animal shelter that needed help feeding and taking care of stray dogs and cats.

Which of these is the best paraphrase of that sentence?

- Ⓐ Luis wrote an article about helping an animal shelter.
- Ⓑ Luis needed help feeding and taking care of stray dogs and cats.
- Ⓒ Luis showed the class an article about an animal shelter that needed help.
- Ⓓ Luis thought the animal shelter should take better care of its dogs and cats.

20 Read the sentence in the box.

> Other students suggested having pizza, games, and prizes, and even a storytelling center for folk tales about animals.

Which of these is the best paraphrase of that sentence?

- Ⓕ Other students had silly ideas.
- Ⓖ Other students had a lot of good ideas.
- Ⓗ Other students had ideas that would not work.
- Ⓙ Other students did not have any ideas because they just wanted to have fun.

GO ON ➡

READING AND LITERARY ANALYSIS, *continued*

Read the chart. Use it to help you answer items 21, 22, and 23.

Characters	Students	Mr. Yamaguchi
Goal	help the animal shelter	**21**
Actions	**22**	gave the class an assignment helped students divide the work
Outcome	**23**	He was proud and happy.

21 Mr. Yamaguchi's main goal was to —
- Ⓐ help the animal shelter
- Ⓑ meet the students' families
- Ⓒ involve the class in a community project
- Ⓓ give students information about cats and dogs

22 To achieve their goal, the students —
- Ⓕ gave speeches
- Ⓖ read the newspaper
- Ⓗ bought cats and dogs
- Ⓙ held a family fun night

23 You know that the students reached their goal because —
- Ⓐ Ms. Taylor cried
- Ⓑ Mr. Yamaguchi was pleased
- Ⓒ they collected lots of pet food
- Ⓓ they had fun with their families

24 The assignment was different from other class assignments because the students had to —
- Ⓕ perform community service
- Ⓖ read the newspaper and write
- Ⓗ work together in small groups
- Ⓙ complete and turn in assignments

25 Read the sentence in the box.

> People poured into the classroom like a great flood.

The writer uses this simile to show that —
- Ⓐ the floor of the classroom was wet
- Ⓑ the people had good things to drink
- Ⓒ the people did not know what to do
- Ⓓ many people came to the classroom

26 Mr. Yamaguchi let the class choose the topic because he wanted the students to —
- Ⓕ read a textbook
- Ⓖ help the animals
- Ⓗ be excited about learning
- Ⓙ invite their parents to a school event

27 Based on their response to his idea, most of Luis's classmates probably —
- Ⓐ loved animals
- Ⓑ never owned pets
- Ⓒ did not care about the community
- Ⓓ thought the project would be easy

28 Based on the response of the class, the speech that Luis gave was probably —
- Ⓕ boring
- Ⓖ inspiring
- Ⓗ hopeless
- Ⓙ humorous

© Hampton-Brown

DIRECTIONS Read the passage.

Two Dreamers, One Goal

Guion Bluford: From Dreamer to Space Engineer

By the time he was a teenager, Guion Bluford knew what he wanted to do with his life. He wanted to be a space engineer. In fact, he dreamed of becoming involved in exploring outer space.

Guion knew he would have to study very hard to make his dream come true. He went to college and studied science and math. After college, he joined the United States Air Force and learned to fly.

Guion got closer to his dream in 1978 when he was accepted into the astronaut training program. Eventually, he became a crew member of the space shuttle *Challenger*. On August 30, 1983, Guion Bluford became the first African American astronaut to fly in space. Guion was part of three more space missions before he left the U.S. space program. He then became a full-time engineer.

Mae Jemison: From Dreamer to Astronaut

When Mae Jemison was a little girl, she used to watch space flights on television. It was not surprising that she focused her life on becoming an astronaut. She got a good start by delving into the science and astronomy bookshelves at the library. She also enjoyed reading science-fiction stories. Her interest in science and her passion for reading helped her graduate from high school when she was only sixteen years old.

Mae went to college to study engineering and African American studies. After college she went to medical school. For several years, she worked as a doctor in Africa and the United States, but she did not forget her dream. She applied to the astronaut training program and was accepted in 1987.

On September 12, 1992, Mae Jemison settled into the space shuttle *Endeavor* for an eight-day adventure. She became the first African American woman to fly into space. After her space flight, she became a college science professor and founded a space-age technology company.

GO ON ➡

READING AND LITERARY ANALYSIS, *continued*

DIRECTIONS Think about the passage on page 34. Then read each item carefully. Choose the best answer. Mark your answer.

29 Mae Jemison was different from Guion Bluford because Mae —

Ⓐ worked as a doctor

Ⓑ joined the Air Force

Ⓒ flew on a space shuttle

Ⓓ was interested in science

30 Which of these is true for both Guion Bluford and Mae Jemison?

Ⓕ Both went to college to study.

Ⓖ Each became a college professor.

Ⓗ Each learned how to fly airplanes.

Ⓙ Both graduated early from high school.

31 Which word best describes both Guion Bluford and Mae Jemison?

Ⓐ funny

Ⓑ ordinary

Ⓒ frightened

Ⓓ successful

32 According to the passage, you can conclude that Mae Jemison was a —

Ⓕ hard teacher

Ⓖ good student

Ⓗ difficult child

Ⓙ private person

DIRECTIONS Read the poem. Then read each item carefully. Choose the best answer. Mark your answer.

> ## One Choice for Me
>
> 1 Miguel wants to be a doctor,
> 2 And wear a coat as white as snow.
> 3 Lisa wants to be a gardener,
> 4 And plant flowers in a row.
> 5 Jamil wants to write songs.
> 6 Notes dance like butterflies in his mind.
> 7 Yuki wants to help the homeless.
> 8 She is really sweet and kind!
> 9 But when I think of the future,
> 10 One thought shines like a jewel.
> 11 I want to be a teacher,
> 12 With students all day at school!

33 Read lines 1 and 2 from the poem. Which of these are being compared in the simile?

Ⓐ snow and Miguel

Ⓑ Miguel and a doctor

Ⓒ a white coat and snow

Ⓓ a doctor and a white coat

34 Read line 6 from the poem. The poet uses this simile to show that Jamil thinks a lot about —

Ⓕ noise

Ⓖ music

Ⓗ insects

Ⓙ dancers

35 Which of these lines from the poem contains a simile?

Ⓐ And plant flowers in a row.

Ⓑ She is really sweet and kind!

Ⓒ With students all day at school!

Ⓓ One thought shines like a jewel.

© Hampton-Brown

GO ON

DIRECTIONS Read the passage. Then read each item carefully. Choose the best answer. Mark your answer.

A Woman Ahead of Her Time

When Jade Snow Wong was a young woman, she dreamed of doing something unimaginable. Although many Chinese American women were expected to seek marriage, Jade dreamed of being independent. She didn't want to find success through a husband. She wanted to find it on her own.

Jade grew up in Chinatown in San Francisco before World War II. From the time Jade was a child, people noticed her intelligence. Her parents, who owned a shop, wanted Jade to marry and adopt their traditional Chinese lifestyle. Jade, however, was determined to go to college and become a more-than-average person.

In college, Jade became fascinated with Chinese pottery. Later she decided on a career that would let her shape beautiful objects out of clay.

Jade's father gave her a studio in a section of a store he owned. Visitors and tourists saw her pottery and began to buy pieces. To sell more of her work, Jade wrote to stores outside San Francisco. She traveled across America to solicit their business. At the time, asking for business was something that women almost never did.

Jade truly believed that she could be successful, and success finally came. She was asked to display her work at the Metropolitan Museum of Art in New York. Other shows followed. Then Jade was invited to teach a special course on pottery at Mills College, in Northern California.

In addition to these successes, Jade also became a writer. Her popular book, *Fifth Chinese Daughter*, tells about growing up in a traditional Chinese family.

---

stuc•co *n.* **1.** a fine plaster used to decorate walls inside buildings. **2.** a hard material used to cover outside walls.

stu•dent *n.* a person who goes to school; a learner.

stu•di•o *n.* **1.** the working place of a painter or an artist. **2.** a place where movies are made. **3.** a place for broadcasting radio shows. **4.** a small apartment.

stu•di•ous *adj.* **1.** working hard to learn. **2.** related to studying.

---

36 When you are independent, you are —

- Ⓕ on your own
- Ⓖ in search of success
- Ⓗ young and intelligent
- Ⓙ dreaming of something

37 If something is traditional, it is

- Ⓐ rich
- Ⓑ usual
- Ⓒ exciting
- Ⓓ difficult

38 In this article, the word studio means —

- Ⓕ a tourist shop
- Ⓖ a small apartment
- Ⓗ the working place of an artist
- Ⓙ a place where movies are made

39 The word solicit means —

- Ⓐ to buy
- Ⓑ to solve
- Ⓒ to make
- Ⓓ to ask for

© Hampton-Brown

GO ON ➡

LANGUAGE SKILLS

DIRECTIONS Below is a short bigraphy about Samuel Goldwyn. Read the biography. Then read each item carefully. Choose the best answer. Mark your answer.

The larger the goal, the harder the work. Samuel Goldwyn came from a family that was poor than most other families, but **1** through hard work he went on to achieve his goal. Samuel moved to the United States at the age of thirteen. He wanted to start a new **2** life there.

Samuel's first job in New York was in a glove factory. He worked longer hours than **3** the other workers, but he had other dreams. He wanted to get into the brand-new world of motion pictures. He knew nothing about **4**

movies. He worked with other people in motion-picture companies, but decided it would be a more bigger challenge to start his **5** own company.

Samuel Goldwyn knew what he had to do. If he picked the best writers, actors, and directors, _____. Before long, **6** Samuel Goldwyn Presents became the more important movie company in **7** Hollywood. It is clear that Samuel Goldwyn became a famous movie maker. His name **8** still appears on movies today.

40 In number 1, poor is best written as —
- Ⓕ poorer
- Ⓖ poorest
- Ⓗ more poorer
- Ⓙ as it is written

41 The best way to combine the sentences in number 2, is —
- Ⓐ thirteen if he wanted
- Ⓑ thirteen after he wanted
- Ⓒ thirteen because he wanted
- Ⓓ thirteen although he wanted

42 In number 3, longer hours is best written —
- Ⓕ long hours
- Ⓖ longest hours
- Ⓗ most long hours
- Ⓙ as it is written

43 The best way to combine the sentences in number 4, is —
- Ⓐ pictures, when he knew
- Ⓑ pictures, since he knew
- Ⓒ pictures, where he knew
- Ⓓ pictures, although he knew

44 In number 5, more bigger is best written —
- Ⓕ bigger
- Ⓖ more big
- Ⓗ most bigger
- Ⓙ as it is written

45 Which of the following should be added to number 6 to make it a complete sentence?
- Ⓐ in the world
- Ⓑ he could find
- Ⓒ then he would succeed
- Ⓓ and costumes and lighting

46 In number 7, more important is best written —
- Ⓕ importantest
- Ⓖ importanter
- Ⓗ most important
- Ⓙ as it is written

47 The best way to combine the sentences in number 8, is —
- Ⓐ movie maker since his name
- Ⓑ movie maker while his name
- Ⓒ movie maker before his name
- Ⓓ movie maker though his name

GO ON

LANGUAGE SKILLS, *continued*

DIRECTIONS Read the passage. Then read each item carefully. Choose the best answer. Mark your answer.

More than anything, Pablo wanted to be on the school football team. He worked out every day on school. He played football
<u>on school</u>. He played football
1
each weekend _____. He read books
2
<u>about football</u> and watched all of the games
3
on TV.

After months of training, Pablo felt he had prepared as well as he could. He was ready to try out for the team.

Tryouts were held <u>to August</u>. A hundred
4
boys wanted to play, but only 45 could be on the team. Pablo did his very best, and when the final list <u>at players</u> was posted
5
<u>in the gym door</u>, his name was on it!
6
Pablo had a great season. In the final game, he caught a touchdown pass to help his team win its first championship in 27 years.

48 In number 1, <u>on school</u> is best written —
- Ⓕ after school
- Ⓖ when school
- Ⓗ above school
- Ⓙ as it is written

49 Which of the following should be added to number 2 to best complete the sentence?
- Ⓐ to his friends
- Ⓑ of his friends
- Ⓒ over his friends
- Ⓓ with his friends

50 In number 3, <u>about football</u> is best written —
- Ⓕ at football
- Ⓖ beside football
- Ⓗ around football
- Ⓙ as it is written

51 In number 4, <u>to August</u> is best written —
- Ⓐ in August
- Ⓑ on August
- Ⓒ up August
- Ⓓ as it is written

52 In number 5, <u>at players</u> is best written —
- Ⓕ in players
- Ⓖ of players
- Ⓗ against players
- Ⓙ as it is written

53 In number 6, <u>in the gym door</u> is best written —
- Ⓐ on the gym door
- Ⓑ from the gym door
- Ⓒ under the gym door
- Ⓓ as it is written

STOP

Section 2: Writing

PROCESS AND STRATEGIES

DIRECTIONS Read about the description Ahmad plans to write. Then read each item carefully. Choose the best answer. Mark your answer.

> Ahmad plans to write a description of Sandra Cisneros, the author of *The House on Mango Street*. As a girl, Cisneros moved frequently with her family between Mexico City and Chicago. Now she is a respected writer who lives in San Antonio, Texas.

1 When Ahmad writes his description, he will try to help the reader —

- Ⓐ write like Sandra Cisneros
- Ⓑ understand facts about Mexico
- Ⓒ imagine the house on Mango Street
- Ⓓ picture what Sandra Cisneros is like

2 The first sentence of Ahmad's description should introduce Cisneros and —

- Ⓕ tell where she lives
- Ⓖ grab the reader's interest
- Ⓗ give a summary of her life
- Ⓙ tell why he is describing her

3 Read the simile that Ahmad wrote.

> Cisneros lives in a house that is as purple as a plum.

Good descriptions include similes because they help the reader —

- Ⓐ picture something better
- Ⓑ appreciate poetic writing
- Ⓒ summarize the description
- Ⓓ understand the writer's feelings

4 Ahmad is ready to revise his writing. What should he do now?

- Ⓕ make a character map
- Ⓖ make a final copy of his writing
- Ⓗ discuss his writing with a partner
- Ⓙ think of other people to write about

GO ON ➤

DIRECTIONS Read the draft of the description that Ahmad wrote. Then read each item carefully. Choose the best answer. Mark your answer.

A Colorful Writer

(1) Sandra Cisneros is a writer. (2) She lives in a house that is as purple as a plum. (3) She has dark hair and eyes that glow. (4) She wrote a book called *The House on Mango Street*. (5) Even the name of the street is colorful!

(6) I think Sandra's mind is full of colors, too. (7) Maybe she sees the bright colors of the dreses Mexican women wear. (8) Maybe she sees the colors of the sky over Chicago and Mexico, where she grew up. (9) At night, does she see the silver stars of her dreams?

(10) Sandra's childhood wasn't the more happy time of her life. (11) In Chicago, she lived in poor neighborhoods. (12) The walls were gray and cracked. (13) Her life seemed shabby to her.

(14) Sandra kept many colors inside her heart. (15) She escaped into books and wrote secret stories. (16) As she grew, she learned to express her ideas to other people. (17) She learned that she could be as bright as she wished to be in the world. (18) She could even live on a purple house!

© Hampton-Brown

GO ON

PROCESS AND STRATEGIES, *continued*

5 Ahmad wants to rewrite sentence 1 to grab his reader's interest. How should he rewrite it?

Ⓐ Sandra Cisneros is funny.

Ⓑ Sandra Cisneros is interesting.

Ⓒ Sandra Cisneros writes books.

Ⓓ Sandra Cisneros must love the colors of the rainbow.

6 What change, if any, should be made in sentence 7?

Ⓕ Change *sees* to **see**

Ⓖ Change *dreses* to **dresses**

Ⓗ Change *Mexican* to **mexican**

Ⓙ Make no change

7 Ahmad wants to make sentence 8 more specific. He should change "she sees the colors of the sky" to —

Ⓐ she sees the colors of the skies

Ⓑ she sees all the colors of the sky

Ⓒ she looks at the colors of the sky

Ⓓ she sees the blues and pinks of the sky

8 What change, if any, should be made in sentence 10?

Ⓕ Change *her* to **their**

Ⓖ Change *wasn't* to **wasnt**

Ⓗ Change *more happy* to **happiest**

Ⓙ Make no change

9 How can Ahmad improve sentence 12?

Ⓐ Delete the words *and cracked*

Ⓑ Change *The walls* to **All the walls**

Ⓒ Change *The walls* to **The walls of her house**

Ⓓ Change *gray and cracked* to **gray or cracked**

10 Which of these is the best way to improve sentence 13?

Ⓕ She did not like her shabby life.

Ⓖ Her life seemed very shabby to her.

Ⓗ Her life seemed as shabby as a worn-out coat.

Ⓙ Her life was just so totally shabby, it wasn't even funny.

11 What change, if any, should be made in sentence 14?

Ⓐ Change *many* to **much**

Ⓑ Change the period to a question mark

Ⓒ Change *Sandra* to **Sandra and her family**

Ⓓ Make no change

12 What change, if any, should be made in sentence 18?

Ⓕ Delete *could*

Ⓖ Change *on* to **in**

Ⓗ Put *purple* after **house**

Ⓙ Make no change

© Hampton-Brown

STOP

WRITTEN COMPOSITION: CHARACTER SKETCH

DIRECTIONS Read the writing prompt, then write your character sketch on a separate sheet of paper.

WRITING PROMPT

Think of a real or an imaginary person who has achieved a goal. Write a character sketch to describe that person to your classmates. Describe the person's thoughts, feelings, and actions. Tell how the person looks.

Coming Full Circle

- Section 1: Reading and Language, pages 44–54
- Section 2: Writing, pages 55–58

Section 1: Reading and Language

VOCABULARY

DIRECTIONS Read each item carefully. Then choose the best answer. Mark your answer.

1 An <u>annex</u> is a —
- Ⓐ type of diary
- Ⓑ box for treasures
- Ⓒ library below ground
- Ⓓ part added to a building

2 When you <u>bother</u> to do something, you —
- Ⓕ refuse to do it
- Ⓖ do it at a later time
- Ⓗ make an effort to do it
- Ⓙ admit you cannot do it

3 A <u>colonizer</u> is a —
- Ⓐ volcano that suddenly erupts
- Ⓑ person who studies medicine
- Ⓒ machine that measures mountains
- Ⓓ plant or animal that moves to a new place

4 A <u>crater</u> is a —
- Ⓕ large rock shot into the air
- Ⓖ road at the bottom of a valley
- Ⓗ mountain that is ready to explode
- Ⓙ bowl-shaped hole at the top of a volcano

5 Something that is <u>damp</u> is a little —
- Ⓐ wet
- Ⓑ dark
- Ⓒ dirty
- Ⓓ strange

6 An <u>eruption</u> is a —
- Ⓕ blast
- Ⓖ basin
- Ⓗ bulge
- Ⓙ boulder

7 A <u>flow</u> is a —
- Ⓐ living plant
- Ⓑ cooling gas
- Ⓒ falling rock
- Ⓓ moving stream

8 Another word for <u>force</u> is —
- Ⓕ heat
- Ⓖ layer
- Ⓗ slope
- Ⓙ power

9 An <u>impression</u> is —
- Ⓐ an idea
- Ⓑ a reason
- Ⓒ a question
- Ⓓ a prediction

10 To <u>matter</u> is to be —
- Ⓕ silent
- Ⓖ hopeful
- Ⓗ important
- Ⓙ dangerous

11 When you are <u>preoccupied</u>, you are —
- Ⓐ taking a nap
- Ⓑ practicing a sport
- Ⓒ thinking about something
- Ⓓ preparing to visit relatives

12 <u>Pressure</u> is the —
- Ⓕ boiling point of melted rock
- Ⓖ return of plant life to an area
- Ⓗ power of one thing pushing against another
- Ⓙ level of noise measured during an earthquake

13 When you <u>shiver</u>, you —
- Ⓐ run for help
- Ⓑ shout for joy
- Ⓒ shake with cold
- Ⓓ raise your voice

14 To <u>survive</u> is to —
- Ⓕ record observations in a book
- Ⓖ discover something from the past
- Ⓗ travel through unexplored lands
- Ⓙ live through a dangerous event or time

15 To <u>wither</u> is to —
- Ⓐ grow large and tall
- Ⓑ act angry and cruel
- Ⓒ search near and far
- Ⓓ become dry and die

GO ON ➡

VOCABULARY, continued

DIRECTIONS Read the sentence in each box. Then read the item carefully.
Choose the best answer. Mark your answer.

 16

> Scientists can sometimes predict
> when a volcano will erupt.

**The root *dict* means "to say." The word *predict*
probably means to —**

- Ⓕ speak loud
- Ⓖ tell in advance
- Ⓗ find out the reason
- Ⓙ think about the problem

 17

> A volcanic eruption is always
> extraordinary!

**The root *extra* means "beyond." The word
extraordinary probably means —**

- Ⓐ hidden
- Ⓑ specific
- Ⓒ amazing
- Ⓓ dangerous

 18

> Not long after an eruption,
> new plants begin to bloom and
> intermix on the mountainside.

**The root *inter* means "among" or "between."
The word *intermix* probably means to —**

- Ⓕ push away
- Ⓖ be the same
- Ⓗ follow behind
- Ⓙ grow together

 19

> New plants and returning animals
> revive an area that has been
> damaged by an eruption.

**The root *viv* means "to live." The word *revive*
probably means to —**

- Ⓐ take care of
- Ⓑ have interest in
- Ⓒ give life back to
- Ⓓ be important for

GO ON ➡

DIRECTIONS Read the passage and study the time line. Then read each item carefully. Choose the best answer. Mark your answer.

A Taste of Cocoa

A Bitter Discovery

Have you ever wondered where chocolate comes from? This delicious treat is made from the beans of the cacao tree. Cacao trees grow in tropical climates. Today, most of the cacao beans in the world are produced in Brazil and some countries along the west coast of Africa.

About 2,400 years ago, the Maya Indians of Central America grew cacao beans as a crop. In the 1500s, the Spanish conqueror of Mexico, Hernán Cortés, took some cacao beans back to Spain. The Spanish nobility thought that the chocolate drink made from the beans tasted bitter. In time, however, hot chocolate and foods made with chocolate became popular in Europe.

In the 1800s, a Dutch chemist figured out how to make cocoa butter and cocoa powder from cacao beans. This led to the invention of chocolate candy. During the Industrial Revolution, machines made it possible to produce chocolate for many people.

From Beans to Candy Bars

How does the bean of the cacao tree become a candy bar? First, chocolate-makers blend beans that have been fermented and dried. They clean the beans and then blend them in different ways to make different flavors. Next, the beans are roasted and cracked. Then they are ground into a fine powder. After that, ingredients such as sugar, vanilla, and milk powder are added. The mixture is then put through a process that makes the chocolate very smooth or fine. Finally, the chocolate is molded into the shape of a piece of candy and then cooled.

Important Events in the History of Chocolate

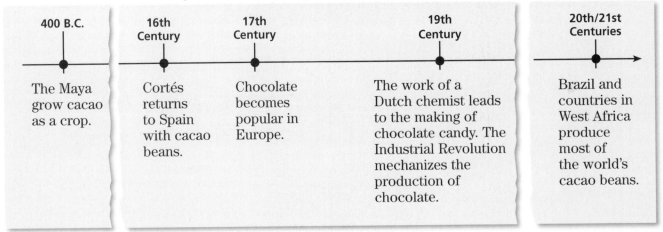

400 B.C.	16th Century	17th Century	19th Century	20th/21st Centuries
The Maya grow cacao as a crop.	Cortés returns to Spain with cacao beans.	Chocolate becomes popular in Europe.	The work of a Dutch chemist leads to the making of chocolate candy. The Industrial Revolution mechanizes the production of chocolate.	Brazil and countries in West Africa produce most of the world's cacao beans.

© Hampton-Brown

GO ON ➡

READING AND LITERARY ANALYSIS, *continued*

Read the chart. Use it to help you answer items 20 and 21.

Cause	Effect
20 _____	Foods made with chocolate became popular in Europe.
A Dutch chemist discovered how to make cocoa butter and cocoa powder.	**21** _____

20 **Which of these goes on the blank line under Cause?**

  Ⓕ Hernán Cortés took cacao beans to Spain.

  Ⓖ Cacao trees were grown throughout Brazil.

  Ⓗ Maya Indians planted cacao trees in Mexico.

  Ⓙ Cacao beans were picked in Central America.

21 **Which of these goes on the blank line under Effect?**

  Ⓐ Cacao trees were grown.

  Ⓑ Bitter drinks were served.

  Ⓒ Cacao beans were roasted.

  Ⓓ Chocolate candies were invented.

22 **When were cacao beans first brought to Spain?**

  Ⓕ when Cortés returned to Spain in the 1500s

  Ⓖ after hot chocolate became popular in Europe

  Ⓗ before the Maya grew cacao about 2,400 years ago

  Ⓙ when Brazil became a major producer of cacao beans

23 **When was chocolate candy first made?**

  Ⓐ in 400 B.C.

  Ⓑ in the 1500s

  Ⓒ in the 1800s

  Ⓓ in the 21st century

24 **Why do chocolate-makers blend beans in different ways?**

  Ⓕ to create fine powders

  Ⓖ to get a variety of flavors

  Ⓗ to make smooth candy bars

  Ⓙ to mold candy into different shapes

© Hampton-Brown

GO ON

DIRECTIONS <u>Skim</u> the passage. Then read each item carefully. Choose the best answer.
Mark your answer.

Forest Fires—Good or Bad?

Most people think that forest fires are problems. Yet research shows that the heat and smoke of forest fires can be helpful. In fact, fires are sometimes needed to help the new plants in forests grow. They play an important role in the life cycle of a forest.

Out of Destruction Comes Life

Young seedlings, growing in the shadow of older trees, seldom receive much light. Forest fires open the forest floor. More light reaches the seedlings and produces a healthier mix of young and old plants.

Smoke Encourages New Growth

When a forest burns, smoke can help bring some seeds to life. Seeds hidden under the soil may start to grow when the smoke reaches them. Scientists can now study different characteristics of seeds to find out whether the seeds are brought to life by smoke.

Fires Affect People, Too

For years, people have been moving into forest areas to live. Forest fires may be good at times for forests, but they can be a serious threat to human residents. They can place them and their property in danger.

How Fires Affect a Forest

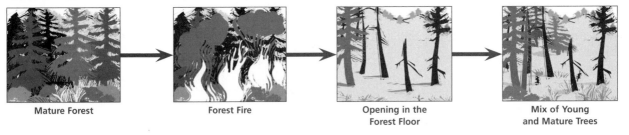

Mature Forest　　　　Forest Fire　　　　Opening in the Forest Floor　　　　Mix of Young and Mature Trees

GO ON ➡

© Hampton-Brown

READING AND LITERARY ANALYSIS, *continued*

25 **When you skim the passage, what should you do?**

Ⓐ Read for details.

Ⓑ Find the answers to questions.

Ⓒ List the names of plants and animals.

Ⓓ Look at the section headings and the diagram.

26 **Which of these questions would be good to write on a notecard before you read?**

Ⓕ How do trees in a forest grow?

Ⓖ How does more light reach seedlings?

Ⓗ How does smoke encourage new growth?

Ⓙ What different kinds of trees grow in a forest?

27 **Which of these questions does the passage answer?**

Ⓐ How do fires affect a forest?

Ⓑ How can we prevent forest fires?

Ⓒ What are the best methods for fighting fires?

Ⓓ What animals are able to survive forest fires?

28 **You have set up a notecard like this one to take notes on the last section. Now read the section and look for answers to the question.**

How do forest fires affect people?

Which of these should not be written on the card?

Ⓕ Some people live in forest areas.

Ⓖ Fires can threaten people's lives.

Ⓗ Fires can cause the loss of property.

Ⓙ Everyone should help prevent forest fires.

GO ON

© Hampton-Brown

DIRECTIONS Read the story. Then read each item carefully. Choose the best answer.
Mark your answer.

The Wind Eagle

As he did every morning, Gluscabi went fishing for salmon. He started to row toward a good fishing spot on the water.

Gluscabi begged, "Wind Eagle! Quiet down! I want to fish!"

The wind didn't listen.

Gluscabi quickly scrambled up the mountain to ask the wind again to calm down. As he climbed, the fierce wind rose up and struck him down, but he crawled on.

When he reached the mountaintop, Gluscabi saw the Wind Eagle. With each beat of the eagle's powerful wings, a giant wind rushed over the land.

"Eagle!" Gluscabi pleaded. "Your wind has grown too strong. Send a young breeze, warm and soft as a whispered secret."

The proud Wind Eagle refused to listen. Without thinking, Gluscabi angrily pushed the great beast into a crevice between the rocks. Its mighty wings could not flap at all, but Gluscabi felt no sympathy for it.

At first Gluscabi fished with joy, but as the days passed, the air became heavy. Then the lake turned still and dark. Finally, the salmon began to die.

Gluscabi did not know how sorry he would feel about what he had done. He realized that by stopping the Wind Eagle, he had gone too far.

Gluscabi ran up the mountain. When he reached the crevice, he called, "Eagle! I will free you if you promise to send only gentle winds."

After a long silence the Wind Eagle answered, "I promise."

When Gluscabi set the eagle free, it began to slowly flap its wings. The air became fresh and sweet again. The salmon recovered and rose to Gluscabi's bait. The land was happy again.

Today we have gentle winds most of the time. Sometimes though, the Wind Eagle forgets its promise, and then fierce winds, hurricanes, and cyclones roar over the land.

GO ON ➡

29 Which of these best describes Gluscabi in the first part of the story?
Ⓐ afraid of nature
Ⓑ happy and joyful
Ⓒ proud of himself
Ⓓ angry and determined

30 Which of these best describes the Wind Eagle?
Ⓕ angry, then sad
Ⓖ wise, then gentle
Ⓗ worried, then angry
Ⓙ stubborn, then helpful

31 What does Gluscabi do when the wind will not let him fish?
Ⓐ He pushes his canoe back to shore.
Ⓑ He catches the Wind Eagle's powerful wings.
Ⓒ He climbs to the crevice to free the Wind Eagle.
Ⓓ He climbs the mountain to ask the wind to calm down.

32 What happens right after Gluscabi pushes the Wind Eagle into the crevice?
Ⓕ Gluscabi falls off the mountain.
Ⓖ Fierce winds roar over the land.
Ⓗ The air becomes fresh and sweet.
Ⓙ The Wind Eagle cannot flap its wings.

33 What happens right after the air becomes heavy?
Ⓐ The lake turns still and dark.
Ⓑ A breeze whispers over the land.
Ⓒ Gluscabi finds a good fishing spot.
Ⓓ Gluscabi climbs down the mountain.

34 According to the story, hurricanes and cyclones sometimes occur because —
Ⓕ the Wind Eagle is fierce and proud
Ⓖ the Wind Eagle forgets its promise
Ⓗ Gluscabi is not fishing on those days
Ⓙ Gluscabi pulls the eagle out of the crevice

Study the plot diagram for "The Wind Eagle."

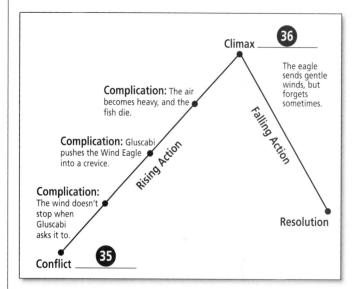

35 Which of these best completes the conflict part of the diagram?
Ⓐ The Wind Eagle cannot get out of the crevice.
Ⓑ Gluscabi has to fish for salmon every morning.
Ⓒ The Wind Eagle promises to send only gentle winds.
Ⓓ Gluscabi cannot fish because the wind is too strong.

36 Which of these best completes the climax part of the diagram?
Ⓕ The Wind Eagle calls out for Gluscabi.
Ⓖ Gluscabi paddles against the strong wind.
Ⓗ Gluscabi rows toward a better fishing spot.
Ⓙ Gluscabi frees the eagle, and the eagle agrees to send gentle winds.

© Hampton-Brown

DIRECTIONS Read the passage. Compare it with "The Wind Eagle," on page 50.
Then read each item carefully. Choose the best answer. Mark your answer.

A Different Way

The first light of dawn touched the tops of the pines as Tiwa crept through the forest. "The air is so still," she thought, listening to her footsteps on the path. "It feels as if something unusual is going to happen."

Tiwa set her basket under an oak tree to gather acorns. Suddenly something flashed in the corner of her eye. She turned. A baby sparrow was falling from a nest!

She ran to the small creature. Its eyes were closed and its beak was open, gasping for breath.

Tiwa knew that if she left the bird on the ground, it would die. She wasn't sure if she should help it, though. Her parents disapproved of interfering with nature. She could hear her mother's voice: "Animals take care of themselves. That is the way of nature. That's the way it's always been."

"But I have to help this bird," Tiwa thought. She scooped it up with a large leaf and placed it gently in her basket. Then she hurried home.

Her mother was cooking outside. "What are you doing with that?" she asked when she noticed the bird. "Where are the acorns?"

"This little sparrow fell from a tree," Tiwa explained. "I had to bring it home to help it."

Tiwa's mother frowned, but her eyes softened when she saw the tiny bird. She searched for a lid with loose weavings. "Your bird will be able to breathe through this," she said as she put the lid on the basket.

Every day Tiwa fed the bird with drops of water dribbled from the end of a twig. When it got stronger, she brought it worms and other bugs. One day she heard it beating its wings inside the basket.

"It's time to let it go," her mother said.

They took the basket outside and Tiwa lifted the lid. The tiny bird soared upward like a burst of light. Tiwa and her mother watched it flutter toward the forest.

"It is good that you helped that bird," her mother admitted in a quiet voice.

"I know," Tiwa said.

© Hampton-Brown

GO ON ➡

READING AND LITERARY ANALYSIS, *continued*

37 Both "The Wind Eagle" and a "A Different Way" are about —

Ⓐ nature

Ⓑ fishing

Ⓒ family life

Ⓓ winter storms

38 Which selection is a fantasy?

Ⓕ "The Wind Eagle" because it tells about hurricanes and cyclones.

Ⓖ "A Different Way" because it tells about events that could really happen.

Ⓗ "A Different Way" because it tells about characters that the writer created.

Ⓙ "The Wind Eagle" because it is tells about events that could not really happen.

39 How is the eagle in "The Wind Eagle" like the sparrow in "A Different Way"?

Ⓐ Both get help.

Ⓑ Both can speak.

Ⓒ Both are powerful.

Ⓓ Both fly into a forest.

40 How are Gluscabi and Tiwa's mother alike?

Ⓕ Both hurt birds.

Ⓖ Both eat salmon and acorns.

Ⓗ Both learn something important.

Ⓙ Both like to interfere with nature.

GO ON ➡

LANGUAGE SKILLS

DIRECTIONS Read the passage. Read each item carefully. Choose the best answer. Mark your answer.

One way to learn about continuity in your family is to make a family tree. People have always kept old letters, pictures, and other informal records of their ancestors. Today, genealogy, or studying family history, <u>has became</u> a
1

popular pastime.

To get started, you can talk to family members <u>which might remember</u> stories.
2

Look at objects <u>who have been</u> in your
3

family a long time. Who knows? Maybe

Grandmother, <u>who</u> trunk is in the attic, has
4

fascinating family papers!

You can often find important dates and places in marriage, birth, and death records. These <u>records have always been</u>
5

an excellent source of information. The <u>Internet have also begun</u> to list information
6

of this type. In the past, <u>it is necessary</u> to
7

travel to find lost family records. Now, documents <u>that have seemed</u> impossible to
8

find show up right on your computer screen!

41 In number 1, **has became** is best written —
- (A) has become
- (B) have become
- (C) have became
- (D) as it is written

42 In number 2, **which might remember** is best written —
- (F) who might remember
- (G) which may remember
- (H) whom might remember
- (J) as it is written

43 In number 3, **who have been** is best written —
- (A) that have been
- (B) which has been
- (C) whom have been
- (D) as it is written

44 In number 4, **who** is best written —
- (F) whom
- (G) which
- (H) whose
- (J) as it is written

45 In number 5, **records have always been** is best written —
- (A) record have always been
- (B) records has always been
- (C) records are always being
- (D) as it is written

46 In number 6, **Internet have also begun** is best written —
- (F) Internet has also begun
- (G) Internet has also began
- (H) Internet have also began
- (J) as it is written

47 In number 7, **it is necessary** is best written —
- (A) it is been necessary
- (B) it is being necessary
- (C) it has been necessary
- (D) as it is written

48 In number 8, **that have seemed** is best written —
- (F) that has seemed
- (G) which has seemed
- (H) who have seemed
- (J) as it is written

STOP

© Hampton-Brown

Section 2: Writing

DIRECTIONS Read about the science report Zita plans to write. Then read each item carefully. Choose the best answer. Mark your answer.

Zita wants to write a science report on the causes of dinosaur extinction. She is particularly interested in the theory that a meteorite—a large chunk of rock from space—killed many dinosaurs by changing the weather.

1 In expository writing, you —

Ⓐ give information
Ⓑ tell a fictional story
Ⓒ express personal feelings
Ⓓ persuade readers to take action

2 In her report, Zita should —

Ⓕ describe her favorite dinosaurs
Ⓖ tell how birds are related to dinosaurs
Ⓗ provide directions to the Science Museum
Ⓙ explain how changes in weather may have affected the dinosaurs

3 Zita wants to elaborate on her topic. What should she do?

Ⓐ Revise the topic.
Ⓑ Tell more about the topic.
Ⓒ Check the facts related to the topic.
Ⓓ Delete text that does not support the topic.

4 Zita wants to edit and proofread her work. She should —

Ⓕ change facts
Ⓖ choose a topic
Ⓗ give an oral report
Ⓙ combine short sentences

© Hampton-Brown

GO ON

DIRECTIONS Read the draft of the science report that Zita wrote. Then read each item carefully. Choose the best answer. Mark your answer.

Why the Dinosaurs Disappeared

(1) For 150 million years, the Earth's motto might have been: "Dinosaurs rule!" (2) Then, millions of years ago, these amazing reptiles disappeared.

(3) Many people have wonder why the dinosaurs became extinct. (4) Did the explosion of a gigantic star kill them? (5) Did smaller animals eat the dinosaurs' egges? (6) Did the dinosaurs die of disease?

(7) According to most scientists, a disaster happened on the Earth 65 million years ago. (8) It killed many dinosaurs and other creatures. (9) It left a crater more than 100 miles across. (10) A meteorite, which was several miles in diameter, hit Mexico's Yucatán Peninsula.

(11) The crash also sent clouds of dust into the air. (12) The Earth grew dark and cold. (13) Plants withered and died in the harsh climate. (14) The dinosaurs who survived the crash lost their food supply and eventually starved.

(15) No one has ever completely solved the mystery of the disappearing dinosaurs but one thing is certain. (16) There are no dinosaurs on the Earth today! (17) It would be incredible if dinosaurs shared the Earth with human beings.

© Hampton-Brown

GO ON

5 What change, if any, should be made to sentences 1 and 2 to introduce the topic and spark the reader's interest?

- Ⓐ For 150 million years, there were dinosaurs on the Earth. Then they disappeared.
- Ⓑ Dinosaurs lived on the Earth for millions of years. Dinosaurs are amazing creatures.
- Ⓒ Dinosaurs walked around on the Earth for millions of years. Some dinosaurs ate plants.
- Ⓓ Make no change

6 What change, if any, should be made in sentence 3?

- Ⓕ Change *became* to **become**
- Ⓖ Change the period to a question mark
- Ⓗ Change *have wonder* to **have wondered**
- Ⓙ Make no change

7 What change, if any, should be made in sentence 5?

- Ⓐ Change *egges* to **eggs**
- Ⓑ Change *smaller* to **more smaller**
- Ⓒ Change *dinosaurs'* to **dynosaurs'**
- Ⓓ Make no change

8 Zita wants to change the order of the sentences in the third paragraph. She should put —

- Ⓕ sentence 7 after sentence 8
- Ⓖ sentence 8 before sentence 7
- Ⓗ sentence 9 before sentence 8
- Ⓙ sentence 10 after sentence 7

9 What is the best way to revise sentence 12 to make the meaning clear?

- Ⓐ The Earth grew very cold and dark.
- Ⓑ Nothing grew on the Earth, which was dark and cold.
- Ⓒ Because of the sun, the Earth never grows dark and cold.
- Ⓓ The dust blocked out the sun, and the Earth grew dark and cold.

10 What change, if any, should be made in sentence 14?

- Ⓕ Change *who* to **that**
- Ⓖ Change *their* to **they're**
- Ⓗ Change *eventually* to **eventual**
- Ⓙ Make no change

11 What change, if any, should be made in sentence 15?

- Ⓐ Change *is* to **are**
- Ⓑ Change *has* to **have**
- Ⓒ Add a comma before *but*
- Ⓓ Make no change

12 Which of these sentences should replace sentence 17 to help sum up the topic of the report?

- Ⓕ Most scientists believe that the meteorite theory explains why.
- Ⓖ Can you imagine bumping into a dinosaur on the way to school?
- Ⓗ The dinosaurs, as you know, disappeared from the Earth long ago.
- Ⓙ The more you learn about dinosaurs, the more you wonder why they became extinct.

STOP

WRITTEN COMPOSITION: REPORT

DIRECTIONS Read the writing prompt, then write your report on a separate sheet of paper.

WRITING PROMPT

Write a guide for new middle school students. Explain how to prepare for the end of the school year. Choose from the following list of ideas to help you start your guide:

1. Plan for and sign up for summer jobs or activities.
2. Get a list of books to read this summer.
3. Study for and complete all final exams.
4. Turn in all make-up or extra-credit assignments.
5. Clean out your locker.

Overcoming Obstacles

Section 1: Reading and Language

VOCABULARY

DIRECTIONS Read each item carefully. Then choose the best answer. Mark your answer.

1 Someone who is <u>boastful</u> —
- Ⓐ brags
- Ⓑ sneaks
- Ⓒ hurries
- Ⓓ whispers

2 A <u>canal</u> is a —
- Ⓕ lake used for sailing
- Ⓖ river that is polluted
- Ⓗ waterway built by people
- Ⓙ stream found in the mountains

3 <u>Capability</u> is another word for —
- Ⓐ ability
- Ⓑ caution
- Ⓒ excitement
- Ⓓ opportunity

4 <u>Cleverness</u> is a kind of —
- Ⓕ habitat
- Ⓖ solution
- Ⓗ research
- Ⓙ intelligence

5 To <u>combat</u> is to —
- Ⓐ flee
- Ⓑ fight
- Ⓒ hatch
- Ⓓ confess

6 A <u>crate</u> is a —
- Ⓕ ripe fruit
- Ⓖ small shed
- Ⓗ wooden box
- Ⓙ field worker

7 An <u>effect</u> is —
- Ⓐ an idea
- Ⓑ a result
- Ⓒ a beginning
- Ⓓ an experiment

8 Something that is <u>endangered</u> may —
- Ⓕ die out
- Ⓖ harm wildlife
- Ⓗ control water
- Ⓙ change location

9 To <u>enroll</u> is to —
- Ⓐ go in
- Ⓑ sign up
- Ⓒ close down
- Ⓓ move away

10 The <u>environment</u> is made up of —
- Ⓕ air, land, and water
- Ⓖ eggs, nests, and shells
- Ⓗ cars, trains, and planes
- Ⓙ people, machines, and buildings

11 <u>Extinction</u> is the —
- Ⓐ flow of water to the sea
- Ⓑ rising of water vapor into air
- Ⓒ end of life for a group of animals
- Ⓓ movement of animals to a warmer climate

12 To <u>interfere</u> is to —
- Ⓕ clean
- Ⓖ drain
- Ⓗ block
- Ⓙ support

13 A <u>marsh</u> is a —
- Ⓐ low, wet grassland
- Ⓑ mythical sea creature
- Ⓒ large, slow-moving mammal
- Ⓓ farm where grapes are grown

14 <u>Pollution</u> makes the Earth —
- Ⓕ cold
- Ⓖ moist
- Ⓗ empty
- Ⓙ unclean

15 When you <u>preserve</u> something, you —
- Ⓐ keep it safe
- Ⓑ change it forever
- Ⓒ sell it for money
- Ⓓ prevent it from growing

GO ON ➤

DIRECTIONS Survey the selection by reading the headings. Then read each section carefully. Choose the best answer to each item. Mark your answer.

The Toda of the Nilgiri Hills

Like animals, groups of people can become endangered, too. The Toda are an example of a people whose way of life is in danger of being lost forever.

Traditional Toda Life

The Toda live in the hills of southern India. Both men and women wear *putkulis*, or white capes decorated with red and black. Water buffalo are very important to their culture. The Toda raise the buffalo and sell their milk. The Toda are known for their love of nature. For instance, they protect animals and use the land with care. They are a peaceful people who do not believe in weapons or fighting. They have a tradition of working together and helping each other.

The Problem

There are very few Toda left. Disease brought by foreign visitors is a main reason for their decline. Today, there are only around 1,000 Toda living in the Nilgiri Hills.

Future of the Toda

The Toda story may have a happy ending, though. A dentist from the area, Dr. Tarun Chhabra, is working hard to make sure that the Toda traditions do not disappear. He and others are helping to rebuild houses and religious buildings in the old way. The people are also selling needlework and other things they make by hand so that others will know about their skill. Slowly, things are getting better for the Toda people.

16 Sara is using the SQ3R strategy to remember the information in this passage. What should Sara do after she reads each section?

- (F) Write questions about the selection.
- (G) Turn the section titles into questions.
- (H) Look at the graphics, charts, and photos.
- (J) Summarize the section in her own words.

17 Which of these would <u>not</u> be a good question to ask before reading the passage?

- (A) Who are the Toda?
- (B) Who visits the Nilgiri Hills?
- (C) What are some Toda traditions?
- (D) What problem do the Toda face?

18 Which of these is the best way for Sara to recite in her own words what the first paragraph says?

- (F) The Toda people live like lost animals.
- (G) The Toda people have a dangerous way of living.
- (H) The animals raised by the Toda people are in danger.
- (J) The Toda people and their customs may be lost forever.

19 Which of these is the best summary of the last section?

- (A) Buffalo are very important to the Toda way of life.
- (B) Dr. Tarun Chhabra lives in a traditional Toda building.
- (C) Thanks to help from a local dentist, the Toda may have a better future.
- (D) The Toda know how to work together and do needlework and other crafts.

GO ON

DIRECTIONS Read the fable. Then read each item carefully. Choose the best answer. Mark your answer.

The Tale of the Black Bull

Part 1

Long ago, on a farm in India, a black calf was born. This calf was so beautiful and so perfect that his owner named him Beauty. The owner gave Beauty the best care and always spoke lovingly to him. The calf grew into a strong mountain of a bull.

Beauty wanted to show his owner how grateful he felt. The bull said, "Why don't you have a contest for all the bulls in the land? See which can pull a hundred carts loaded with heavy stones. You can offer one thousand gold pieces to the winner."

Beauty's owner liked the idea and planned the race. The day of the race, the owner got on Beauty's back. He fiercely whipped the bull and shouted, "Move, worthless beast! Move!" The bull was shocked. He stood still. He wouldn't move. The owner lost the race and his gold.

Part 2

The bull's owner was so sad that he went to bed even though it was noon. Beauty looked into the window of his owner's house.

He asked his owner, "What is the matter?"

"I have lost so much money. I don't know what to do."

Beauty asked, "Why were you so mean during the race? Did the money make you forget that I was your faithful friend?"

His owner did not know what to say.

Beauty suggested, "Have another race for two thousand gold pieces. This time, treat me with kindness and see what happens."

So Beauty's owner did as the bull asked. During the second race, the owner kindly asked Beauty to do a good job and gently stroked his back. Beauty pulled with all his might and easily won the race for his owner.

GO ON

READING AND LITERARY ANALYSIS, *continued*

20 **Read the sentence in the box.**

> The calf grew into a strong mountain of a bull.

The writer's metaphor shows that Beauty was —

Ⓕ shy and quiet

Ⓖ happy and kind

Ⓗ slow and stubborn

Ⓙ large and powerful

21 **Why did the author write this fable?**

Ⓐ to teach a lesson

Ⓑ to make people laugh

Ⓒ to describe life in India

Ⓓ to give information about bulls

22 **In Part 1, why was Beauty grateful?**

Ⓕ He got to be in a contest.

Ⓖ He lived on a farm in India.

Ⓗ He was beautiful and perfect.

Ⓙ His owner took very good care of him.

23 **In the fable, Beauty did not win the first race because —**

Ⓐ the cart was too heavy

Ⓑ he got stuck in the mud

Ⓒ the other bulls scared him

Ⓓ his owner was cruel to him

24 **The writer of the fable believes that —**

Ⓕ hurting animals is wrong

Ⓖ animals cannot be trusted

Ⓗ winning contests is important

Ⓙ animal owners have a hard life

25 **Which of these is the best summary of Part 1?**

Ⓐ A man raises a beautiful bull, but it is not strong enough to win a race.

Ⓑ A man raises a fine bull, but he finds out that he is not good at riding it.

Ⓒ A man loves his bull, but he becomes angry when it grows too big to win a race.

Ⓓ A man raises a bull lovingly, but he loses a race one day when he is mean to the bull.

26 **Which of these is the best summary of Part 2?**

Ⓕ The bull wins a new race when his owner treats him kindly.

Ⓖ The bull works hard to get stronger, and he easily wins his next race.

Ⓗ The bull wants his owner to be rich, so he pulls more carts to win money.

Ⓙ The bull is afraid of his mean owner, so he tries harder and wins his next race.

27 **Which of these is the best summary of the entire fable?**

Ⓐ A man learns that his bull will work hard for him if he treats it well.

Ⓑ A man learns that if he does not yell at his bull, he can win a lot of money.

Ⓒ A man learns that his bull will work hard for him if he pretends to be nice.

Ⓓ A man learns that his beautiful black bull is stronger and wiser than other animals.

GO ON ➡

READING AND LITERARY ANALYSIS, *continued*

DIRECTIONS **Read the letter. Then read each item carefully. Choose the best answer. Mark your answer.**

> Dear Editor:
>
> I read that a dog almost died because it was left in a hot car with the windows rolled up. The owner said he was only gone for a few minutes and thought the dog would be okay. The owner had to pay a fine because he broke the law.
>
> I think we should make the law tougher. People who do this should have their pets taken away. Fines are not stopping people from leaving their dogs in cars with rolled-up windows. If people knew they were going to lose their pets, they might take the time to keep the car windows down when it's hot.
>
> Respectfully,
> Yoko Nakata

28 **Yoko wrote the letter because she wants readers to —**

F make the law tougher

G take away everyone's pets

H use air conditioning in cars

J pay fines for breaking laws

29 **The dog in the car almost died because —**

A it was hit by another car

B the owner had to pay a fine

C it was taken from its owner

D all the windows were rolled up

30 **The best summary of the letter is —**

F Some people do not take good care of their pets.

G When people go shopping, they should leave their pets at home.

H If people rolled down the windows, their pets would run away.

J If people knew they might lose their pets, they would keep their car windows rolled down.

GO ON ➤

DIRECTIONS Read the passage. Then read each item carefully. Choose the best answer. Mark your answer.

Lessons from the Past

We have let the Toda people of southern India nearly disappear. Because of modern ways, it has become hard for them to survive and keep their old way of life alive. You may say, "Why should I care about this? The Toda live far away from my community." That kind of thinking is a big mistake. We should help preserve the Toda culture. We have a lot to learn from these wise people.

The Toda know many things that most modern people do not. For example, they know the importance of respecting the land and the plants that grow on it. The Toda treat the resources of the earth with care. They do not chop down trees. They eat mainly grain and milk so they do not even disturb the soil with plows. If we learned from them, we might be able to use Earth's resources without causing damage.

We could also learn from their feelings about animals. They have a special respect for buffaloes, but they treat all animals with care and kindness. They understand the nature and needs of animals. The Toda raise animals as a way of life. They sell the milk of their cattle and make it into a special butter called ghee. They will not kill animals for either food or clothing.

In addition to teaching us about plants and animals, the Toda can teach us a lot about dealing with people. They do not believe in fighting or harming people to get what they want. When Toda people have a problem, they meet with the older people of the village, or elders. The elders help figure out a solution to the problem with no yelling or arguing. No one gets hurt.

If modern people are smart, they will try to understand the Toda and their brotherhood with all living creatures. For our future, we need to learn the wise ideas from the past.

There are ways you can help endangered peoples, even if they are far away like the Toda. Give whatever you can afford to organizations that help. Also, please help by learning all about endangered peoples. Tell everyone you know what we can learn from them.

31 What has caused the Toda to nearly disappear?
Ⓐ wars
Ⓑ lack of food
Ⓒ modern ways
Ⓓ loss of money

32 The author wants us to agree with his or her point of view. Which of these was <u>most</u> important for the author to include?
Ⓕ a lot of details
Ⓖ interesting facts
Ⓗ persuasive sentences
Ⓙ scientific information

33 The author believes that we need to —
Ⓐ visit India
Ⓑ learn from the past
Ⓒ preserve our own culture
Ⓓ raise animals as a way of life

34 Why do Toda go to elders when they have problems?
Ⓕ They want to avoid fighting.
Ⓖ Elders know about plants and animals.
Ⓗ Elders are better at yelling and arguing.
Ⓙ It is easier than trying to find a solution.

GO ON ➡

READING AND LITERARY ANALYSIS, *continued*

DIRECTIONS Read each poem. Then read each item carefully. Choose the best answer. Mark your answer.

Math Problem

I stare at the problem on my page.
I can't do division tonight!
The numbers are wiggly, squiggly worms.
I wish I could turn out the light.

I scratch my head. I bite my lip.
My brain is a broken machine.
I know I can do this if I try . . .
Yes! The answer is 17!

Riding the Rapids

River wide, river brimming.
Our raft is a leaf,
Spinning, skimming.

River cold, river deep.
Your course is wild.
We dip and leap!

River mighty, river long.
Your rushing waters
Are a mountain song.

---

35 Read the line in the box.

> The numbers are wiggly, squiggly
> worms.

This metaphor shows that the writer thinks the numbers are —

Ⓐ hard to read
Ⓑ slimy and wet
Ⓒ long and dirty
Ⓓ written in a fancy way

36 Read the line in the box.

> My brain is a broken machine.

With this metaphor, the writer is trying to say that he or she —

Ⓕ has a headache
Ⓖ cannot think clearly
Ⓗ needs to go to sleep
Ⓙ is thinking of something else

37 Read the lines in the box.

> Our raft is a leaf,
> Spinning, skimming.

This metaphor shows that the writer thinks the raft is —

Ⓐ old, dry, and wrinkled
Ⓑ being blown by the wind
Ⓒ as colorful as autumn leaves
Ⓓ small and light compared to the river

38 Read the lines in the box.

> Your rushing waters
> Are a mountain song.

With this metaphor, the writer is trying to say that rushing waters —

Ⓕ make the mountains wet
Ⓖ are like dancers in the mountains
Ⓗ make a beautiful noise in the mountains
Ⓙ are something mountain people sing about

GO ON

READING AND LITERARY ANALYSIS, *continued*

DIRECTIONS Read the passage. Look at the poster. Then read each item carefully.
Choose the best answer. Mark your answer.

Play Your Part!

Imagine yourself standing on a stage. Rows and rows of people are staring at you. You speak your lines. Applause! Applause!

This is what you'll experience if you join a local teen theater group. You'll get to act in great plays, like *Peter Pan* and *A Thousand Cranes*. You'll also learn to sing and dance. If you're shy, don't worry! Performing in plays will give you confidence.

Of course, rehearsing and performing take a lot of commitment and time. Thousands of kids, however, are in theater groups. If they can do it, so can you! You don't want to be the only one sitting in the audience.

And think—someday you may be a famous actor, like Oliver Wood. "There's nothing as exciting as performing onstage," says Wood.

So take the challenge and grab a script. If you do, everyone will say, "Bravo!"

Poster

Come and Play!

39 Which sentence encourages you to join a theater group?

Ⓐ You speak your lines.

Ⓑ So take the challenge and grab a script.

Ⓒ Rows and rows of people are staring at you.

Ⓓ Rehearsing and performing take a lot of commitment and time.

40 Which sentence is an example of the bandwagon technique?

Ⓕ If you're shy, don't worry!

Ⓖ You may become famous one day.

Ⓗ Performing in plays will give you confidence.

Ⓙ You don't want to be the only one sitting in the audience.

41 Which sentence is an example of the testimonial technique?

Ⓐ If they can do it, so can you!

Ⓑ Imagine yourself standing on a stage.

Ⓒ "There's nothing as exciting as performing onstage," says Wood.

Ⓓ You'll get to act in great plays, like *Peter Pan* and *A Thousand Cranes*.

42 Look at the poster. All of these help make it effective **except** —

Ⓕ few words

Ⓖ a lot of facts

Ⓗ a good image

Ⓙ a clever message

GO ON

DIRECTIONS Below is a story about Rudy and the Ohlone Indians of the San Francisco Bay area. Read the story. Then read each item carefully. Choose the best answer. Mark your answer.

That was it! Rudy closed the social studies book with a bang. He had become tired of hearing that the Ohlone were not recognized as a living tribe. The problem was that there were so few Ohlone left.

Rudy thought, "We must do something. My parents <u>have taught</u> me how to solve
₁
problems." By sundown, Rudy <u>decide</u>
₂
to have a neighborhood Ohlone festival. By the next month, he <u>have made</u> all the
₃

arrangements. He invited friends whose ancestors <u>had came</u> from the Ohlone tribe.
₄
They decided to make music, tell legends, and perform tribal dances. They prepared to make acorn cakes as their people <u>does</u>
₅
long ago.

"After the festival, many people <u>will have learned</u> about the Ohlone," Rudy
₆
said. "They <u>will have saw</u> that we are here
₇
and proud of our past."

43 In number 1, <u>have taught</u> is best written —
- (A) had taught
- (B) have teached
- (C) will have teached
- (D) as it is written

44 In number 2, <u>decide</u> is best written —
- (F) had decided
- (G) have decided
- (H) were decided
- (J) as it is written

45 In number 3, <u>have made</u> is best written —
- (A) make
- (B) had made
- (C) will has made
- (D) as it is written

46 In number 4, <u>had came</u> is best written as —
- (F) had come
- (G) have came
- (H) were coming
- (J) as it is written

47 In number 5, <u>does</u> is best written —
- (A) had did
- (B) had done
- (C) will have done
- (D) as it is written

48 In number 6, <u>will have learned</u> is best written —
- (F) learned
- (G) has learned
- (H) will have learn
- (J) as it is written

49 In number 7, <u>will have saw</u> is best written —
- (A) will be seen
- (B) will have seen
- (C) will have seed
- (D) as it is written

STOP

Section 2: Writing

PROCESS AND STRATEGIES

DIRECTIONS Read about the persuasive essay that Avi plans to write. Then read each item carefully. Choose the best answer. Mark your answer.

> Avi wants to write a 5-paragraph persuasive essay. He wants to convince his readers to stop buying clothes and jewelry made from animals. He knows that elephants, leopards, and other animals might disappear if things do not change.

1 In his essay, Avi will need to do all of these <u>except</u> —

- Ⓐ explain who his audience is
- Ⓑ give his opinion about an issue
- Ⓒ include facts to support his opinion
- Ⓓ try to convince readers to take action

2 Avi is writing a 5-paragraph essay. Where should he present his arguments?

- Ⓕ Paragraph 1
- Ⓖ Paragraphs 1 and 5
- Ⓗ Paragraphs 2, 3, and 4
- Ⓙ Paragraphs 1, 2, and 3

3 In the final paragraph of his essay, Avi should —

- Ⓐ present the issue and state his position
- Ⓑ give his last argument and sum up his opinion
- Ⓒ sum up his opinion and get his readers to take action
- Ⓓ present his least important argument and give facts and examples

4 What would be the <u>best</u> way for Avi to publish his essay?

- Ⓕ write it in his diary
- Ⓖ show it to his friends
- Ⓗ enter it in a poetry contest
- Ⓙ send it to a local newspaper

GO ON

PROCESS AND STRATEGIES, *continued*

DIRECTIONS Read the draft of the persuasive essay that Avi wrote. Then read each item carefully. Choose the best answer. Mark your answer.

Save the Animals

(1) I like elephants, leopards, tigers, and other animals. (2) Do you like them, too?

(3) Each time an animal is killed, it is like losing a work of art. (4) Elephants and leopards are magnificent creatures. (5) They add beauty and wonder to our world, and there aren't that many left.

(6) Tragically, it is not even necesary to kill elephants, leopards, and other animals to provide people with fancy jewelry and fur. (7) People can buy jewelry made from materials other than ivory, such as gold, silver, and precious stones. (8) They can buy beautiful, warm clothes with imitation fur.

(9) The most important reason to stop the killing is to end the suffering of the animals. (10) Every year, millions of animals in Africa, china, and other places are captured or killed in cruel ways. (11) Painful traps grip the legs of wild cats and other fur-bearing animals. (12) Elephants slaughtered with machine guns. (13) Coyotes and other animals are beaten to death instead of being shot, in order not to damage their fur.

(14) Before I learn about this terrible problem, I had planned to buy a jacket with rabbit fur. (15) Now, I try to do everything I can to stop people from killing animals. (16) There are things you must do, too.

PROCESS AND STRATEGIES, *continued*

5 How should Avi revise sentences 1 and 2 of his persuasive essay?

Ⓐ Elephants and leopards live in Africa. You can visit them there.

Ⓑ Elephants eat plants, but leopards hunt for food. They eat monkeys, baboons, and other animals.

Ⓒ Elephants have ivory tusks, and leopards have tan coats with black spots. I think they are both beautiful animals.

Ⓓ Elephants and leopards lose their lives every day so that people can have jewelry and fur coats. We must stop the killing.

6 Avi wants to provide more evidence to support his position. Which sentence should he add after sentence 5?

Ⓕ Leopards are the most widely distributed wild cats in the world.

Ⓖ It is surprising to think how many species of animals there are in the world.

Ⓗ Did you know that the elephants in Africa are different from the elephants in Asia?

Ⓙ It is sad to think, for example, that only about 4,000 snow leopards are left in the wild.

7 What change, if any, should be made in sentence 6?

Ⓐ Delete *is*

Ⓑ Put a comma after *animals*

Ⓒ Change *necesary* to **necessary**

Ⓓ Make no change

8 Which transition word or phrase should be added to the beginning of sentence 9?

Ⓕ However,

Ⓖ Therefore,

Ⓗ By the way,

Ⓙ For example,

9 What change, if any, should be made in sentence 10?

Ⓐ Change *are* to **is**

Ⓑ Change *china* to **China**

Ⓒ Change *millions* to **millions'**

Ⓓ Make no change

10 What change, if any, should be made in sentence 12?

Ⓕ Change *with* to **to**

Ⓖ Change the period to a question mark

Ⓗ Change *slaughtered* to **are slaughtered**

Ⓙ Make no change

11 What change, if any, should be made in sentence 14?

Ⓐ Change *this* to **these**

Ⓑ Change *rabbit* to **rabit**

Ⓒ Change *learn* to **learned**

Ⓓ Make no change

12 Avi wants to rewrite sentence 16 to help sum up his position with a call to action. How should he rewrite it?

Ⓕ I hope that this essay has convinced you to do what you can, too.

Ⓖ Many other people are also concerned about this sad problem and are doing all they can to help save animals.

Ⓗ You can save animals, too, by not buying ivory jewelry or fur clothes and by supporting organizations that help animals.

Ⓙ No revision is needed.

© Hampton-Brown

STOP

WRITTEN COMPOSITION: LETTER TO THE EDITOR

DIRECTIONS Read the writing prompt, then write your letter on a separate sheet of paper.

WRITING PROMPT

Write a letter to the editor. Tell about a topic that is important to you. State your position and give arguments to convince your readers to take action.

ACKNOWLEDGMENTS

Photographs and Illustrations

Marcia Bateman Walker: p48 (forest fires)
Stone: Cover (©Stone); p23 (kids playing with computer ©Stone)
PhotoEdit: p67 (teens performing a play ©Tom Carter)

Hampton-Brown
P.O. Box 223220
Carmel, CA 93922
1–800–333–3510
www.hampton-brown.com

Printed in the United States of America
ISBN 0-7362-2670-2

05 06 07 08 09 10 11 12 13 14 10 9 8 7 6 5 4 3 2 1